Healing for Body, Soul and Spirit

Healing for Body, Soul and Spirit

An Introduction to Anthroposophical Medicine

Dr Michael Evans and Iain Rodger

Floris Books

First Published in Great Britain in 1992
by Thorsons, an Imprint of HarperCollins*Publishers*

This edition published in 2000 by Floris Books.

British Library CIP Data available

ISBN 0–86315–306–2

Printed in Great Britain
by J.W. Arrowsmith Ltd, Bristol

Contents

Acknowledgments

The authors would like to thank the following for their invaluable help. Dr James Dyson (without whose encouragement and constructive criticism the book would not have been written), Hazel Adams, Dr Jean Brown, Shirley Chalis, Marah Evans, Dr Michaela Glöckler, Tom Huggon, Adrian Large, Dr Broder von Laue, Dr David McGavin, Thomas McKeen, Joan Marcus, Steven Moore, Dr Frank Mulder, Ruth and Bernard Nesfield-Cookson, Bobbie Pounder, Don Ratcliffe, Jennie Rodger, Joan Smith, Shaena Stoehr, Vera Taberner, Ian Wiggle, the Anthroposophical Medical Council, and the Anthroposophical Medical Trust. A debt is also acknowledged to the works of Professor Bernard Lievegoed, Dr Rudolf Treichler and Dr Ari Bos.

Introduction

Recognition of the enormous achievements of conventional medicine has, in recent years, been accompanied by a growing awareness of its limitations and the undesirable side effects of many of its methods of treatment. Patients are less prepared than they were to accept the doctor's prescription without an explanation, and they prefer to have the opportunity to discuss any options which might be available. This more critical appraisal of conventional medicine is reflected in the rapid growth in popularity of alternative approaches, such as homeopathy, herbalism and acupuncture. Most of these are based on philosophies which considerably predate conventional medicine, but they nevertheless benefit many patients.

The conventional approach has advanced medicine in some respects but is based on a limited, materialistic view of the human being which has failed to produce a comprehensive understanding of illness. Some forms of alternative medicine have distinct spiritual philosophies which predate natural science, the study of material phenomena.[1] Turning to these in search of what is lacking in conventional medicine is like trying to turn the clock back, ignoring what has been gained from natural science. What is needed is not a return to the past, but an extension of conventional medicine to take into account both the spiritual and physical sides of the human.

Precisely this is offered by anthroposophical medicine, one of a number of practical applications of the work of the Austrian scientist and philosopher, Rudolf Steiner (1861–1925), the founder of anthroposophy. The name is derived from the Greek *anthropos* (human) and *sophia* (wisdom), which gives something of an indication that anthroposophy involves the development of spiritual wisdom through human self-knowledge. In practice, it is a science of the spirit, extending our knowledge and understanding beyond the foundations laid down by natural science.

Steiner recognized the achievements of natural science in building a picture of the physical world, but sought to go beyond the limits of materialism by rigorously researching the spiritual side of existence. His anthroposophy, or spiritual science, sees humans as beings of body, soul and spirit, and anthroposophical medicine came about as a result of a group of doctors recognizing that this extended physiology had remarkable implications for medical treatment.

During the later years of Steiner's life, people from various professions approached him for guidance on how they might apply the principles of anthroposophy to their particular fields. As well as medicine, this gave birth to new forms of education, art, architecture, caring for the handicapped, agriculture and economics, all of which are now practised worldwide. In the case of medicine, Steiner was invited to address a group of about thirty doctors and medical students who were familiar with anthroposophy. In 1920, he gave a course of lectures which contained insights into human pathology and approaches to therapy, though this could not be considered a systematic introduction to an anthroposophical medicine.[2]

It was through Steiner's collaboration with a Dutch doctor, Ita Wegman (1876-1943), that the foundation for a new medicine was laid. Together, they wrote a book for the medical profession, *Fundamentals of Therapy*, and Dr Wegman opened one of the first anthroposophical clinics at Arlesheim, Switzerland, near the worldwide centre for anthroposophy at Dornach. She later became the first leader of the Medical Section of the School of Spiritual Science at Dornach.[3]

As Steiner was not a medical doctor, he worked with qualified practitioners in the development of anthroposophical medicine. He insisted that it should extend conventional practice rather than become an alternative. To that end, all anthroposophical doctors must qualify first in conventional medicine, then do further study to gain an understanding of the human being in health and illness from a spiritual scientific point of view. This widens the scope of their work beyond conventional practice, and means that anthroposophical doctors can be consulted about any medical problem.

The main aim of anthroposophical medicine is to stimulate the natural healing forces in the patient. These are the life forces which maintain the physical body and oppose decay. They comprise a body of non-physical formative forces, called by Steiner the etheric body, and are particularly active in growth and nutrition. Humans are also conscious beings, aware of their environment and emotionally responsive. This awareness comes from having a third *body*, called the astral body, which is particularly active in the nervous system. Finally, people also know themselves to be independent conscious beings, and have the power to change themselves inwardly. This points to the fourth element of the human: the spiritual core, or ego, which particularly expresses itself in muscular activity and the blood.[4]

These four elements interrelate to form a whole, which must be treated as a whole if the patient is to be helped. Anthroposophical doctors seek to understand illnesses in terms of the way the four aspects interrelate. For example, there is a perpetual tendency towards ill-health because the activity of consciousness has a catabolic, or breaking-down, effect on the physical body. The anabolic, or building-up, forces of the etheric body must constantly combat these effects for good health to be maintained. However, if the etheric forces are themselves too powerful, the imbalance again results in illness. Good health is dependent on these opposing tendencies being kept in equilibrium.

The highly complex picture of the human which emerged through Steiner's work can be difficult to grasp. After all, anthroposophical medicine starts with conventional teaching about the physical body and extends this picture with three further elements. But it can easily be understood that everyday experiences of thoughts, feelings and will-power call for an extension of the natural scientific model, simply because natural science excludes anything not physically measurable. This is where spiritual science can build on the understanding of the physical realm gained through natural science, and extend the frontiers of our knowledge.

Physical perception is limited by the bodily senses, but thinking has no such limits. For example, the concepts of mathematics are not sense-perceptible. The spiritual realm might not be perceived directly with the bodily senses but, with careful observation and disciplined thinking, anyone can gain an understanding

of spiritual science. However, it is possible to go further. Steiner
describes how higher forms of perception can be developed
which enable people to perceive the spiritual realm directly. It
was through his own development of these faculties that he was
able to do the researches on which his descriptions of the spiritual realm were based.

Steiner had the ability to perceive spiritual phenomena in addition to the faculty of perception of the physical environment with
which most people are born. He maintained that everyone had latent organs for spiritual perception which they could develop
through their own efforts.[5] At present, most people are cut off
from direct experience of the spiritual realm in much the same
way that visual images of the physical world are denied to the
blind. However, just as the blind can have other experiences of the
physical world, and can compare these with concepts reported by
sighted people, so can those without developed powers of spiritual perception compare their experiences with anthroposophical
knowledge.

For example, the ideas that anthroposophical medicine adds to
conventional practice might seem strange to someone whose education was based on natural science. But this should encourage
neither blind faith nor blind disbelief. If the ideas are thought
through with an open mind, they can be assessed on their own
merits. The achievements of anthroposophical medicine in practice can also be assessed.

At present, anthroposophical medical work is most widely developed in Germany, the Netherlands and Switzerland, where
there are several hospitals and many general practitioners. All are
fully recognized and funded by state and private medical insurance schemes. In the English-speaking world, it has taken longer
for Steiner's work to become widely known, although interest in
this approach is growing steadily. In the UK, anthroposophical
medicine is practised both within the National Health Service and
privately.

This book has been written to establish a wider understanding
of anthroposophical medicine and to meet the demands of growing interest worldwide. It is intended primarily for a general read-
ership but, it is hoped, will also be of use to health care

professionals who wish to broaden their approach to therapy. Some concepts have had to be simplified because of limited space but, for the benefit of readers who wish to pursue deeper explanations, comprehensive references to further reading have been given.

It must be understood that this book is not a manual for treatment by unqualified persons. It does not replace proper consultation with a doctor, nor does it serve as a training manual. Comprehensive lists will be found at the back which show how to obtain further information, including where to obtain anthroposophical treatment or apply for training in anthroposophical medical methods.

1. Extending the Art and Science of Medicine

Anthroposophical medicine has a growing reputation for its methods of treatment and offers a new approach to meeting the demands of a rapidly changing world. It should not be confused with alternative therapies, as it is firmly based on the knowledge and experience of conventional medicine. The difference is that anthroposophical practice treats the non-physical (or spiritual) elements of the patient as well as the physical.

Working with such elements to extend the range of conventional practice does not make anthroposophical medicine vague or imprecise. All anthroposophical doctors must first qualify in the conventional training, then complete postgraduate studies which add another three elements to the conventional concept of the physical body. These offer a more complete picture of the human being and are called, in anthroposophical terminology, the etheric body, astral body and ego.[1]

They are non-material, spiritual elements, common to everyone though they cannot be perceived with the physical senses. It should be understood that describing them as spiritual does not imply that anthroposophical medicine is based on beliefs, religious or otherwise. It is based on the methods of spiritual science, which has the same rigour and discipline as natural science, but extends the boundary of what is observed beyond the physical world.

Conventional medicine as we know it is derived from natural science, the study of material phenomena — whatever can be weighed, measured or counted. In the last five hundred years, natural science has hugely expanded our understanding of the world around us. Although many of the early scientists were persecuted for their discoveries, they were inspired by this new method of enquiry as they no longer had to rely on traditional religious and philosophical teachings. For us today, this spirit of independent enquiry is as important a legacy as the brilliant achievements of natural science in technology and medicine.

The modern scientific view of the world gradually evolved through one set of discoveries building upon another. The pioneers made their greatest contributions in the fields of astronomy and physics, producing formulae to describe the apparent movements of the planets with respect to the sun. In the seventeenth century, Sir Isaac Newton proposed concepts of force and gravity, through which the movements of the planets were explained by the same formulae that described the way inert objects fell to earth. The basic laws of chemistry began to be formulated when it was discovered that, by weighing inorganic materials before and after chemical reactions had taken place, it was possible to make mathematical descriptions of those reactions.

In Renaissance Italy, an interest in human anatomy prompted artists (notably Leonardo da Vinci) to dissect corpses in order to make the first detailed drawings of the inside of the body. The modern discipline of anatomy grew out of these studies of dead bodies. Similarly, observation and measurement of the functions of human and animal bodies and their organs led to the gradual development of physiology — essentially the methods of physics applied to living organisms. Biochemistry also emerged — essentially the methods of chemistry applied to living things.

These three sciences — anatomy, physiology and biochemistry are taught as basics to all medical students. The principles of each were derived from study of the non-living, but their methods have been applied to the living — to plants, animals and people Because of this, modern science (including medicine) presents an incomplete picture of the world. As will be seen, the laws that relate to inert matter should only be applied to the physical aspects of living things. They do not take into account their life, soul and spiritual dimensions and, therefore, a further science is called for to complete the picture. This is the role of spiritual science, or anthroposophy.

The whole of life is characterized by processes, such as the circulation of the blood, the flow of substances in and out of the liver, and digestive activity. Natural scientific examinations of these processes reduce them to mechanical systems and chemical reactions, typically breaking up the organism to be studied and analysing the parts outside their normal environments. This freezes the physical expression of the process into a form which can be dealt with in the laboratory, but fails to explain fully its role within the living being. It might be said that natural science tends to analyse a snapshot of a process rather than the process itself.

Anthroposophy differs from this approach by regarding the processes as expressions of spiritual principles. It is these higher principles underlying the physical realm that have to be grasped before the life element (or etheric body) can be understood. If the activity involved in a life process is studied, rather than an isolated snapshot, a step is taken towards understanding that element which organizes inert matter into a complex living body.

Wherever life prevails, the normal behaviour of matter is modified, or even reversed. For example, lifeless matter tends always towards a state of disorganization. A stone wall breaks down into dust through erosion; a hot kettle returns to the same temperature as its surroundings when removed from the heat source. However, in plants, animals and humans, matter is organized into complex physical bodies. As long as the life element is present, the high state of organization is preserved. But when it departs, at death, the matter breaks down again into a disorganized state — it returns to *dust*.

By way of another example of how life modifies the laws of the physical realm, it can be observed that inert matter falls predictably under the influence of gravity. Plants, however, grow up from the ground towards the sun, in opposition to gravity. It is, of course, recognized that they are still subject to gravity, and that ripe apples fall to the ground. The point is that the plant draws mineral substances from the earth, organizes them in accordance with a predetermined structure, and endows the whole with an ability to oppose gravity.

At medical school, students learn about the anatomy of the whole body, the physiology of the various organs, the tissues that make up the organs (histology), the cells that form the tissues, and

the biochemical processes that take place between the molecules
that make up the cells. Although not necessarily recognized, there
is an acceptance in contemporary medicine that, when an illness
can be described on a cellular or molecular level, the explanation
in terms of the most minute elements is the most fundamental.

This approach has evolved in tandem with the scientists' ability to analyse ever-smaller constituent parts, and stems particularly from the last century, when refinements in microscope
technology made possible the discovery of cells. A German
pathologist, Rudolf Virchow, said that all living things, including
humans, were made up of cells. When people became ill, he said,
it was because their cells had become ill. If we could understand
how the cells became ill, we would understand how people became ill.[2] His simplistic ideas formed the basis of modern pathology, the science of bodily diseases.

The tendency to look for an isolated cause of a disease is carried over into diagnosis. What a patient experiences and what the
doctor can observe directly form only the starting-point for describing an illness. The more the description is put in terms of
minute elements, such as cellular changes, the more fundamental
it is judged to be. This determination to seek explanations in
terms of the smallest parts falls into a school of thought known as
reductionism, and is one of the most characteristic features of
conventional medicine.

Let us suppose a patient is losing weight, trembling, has a rapid
pulse, is eating more than usual and is possibly rather hyperactive. The illness may be diagnosed as hyperthyroidism (overactivity of the thyroid, a gland in the neck which regulates the rate
of metabolism through the production of a hormone, thyroxine).
Attention shifts from the patient as a whole to one organ. Blood
tests are done to see if thyroxine is present in increased concentrations, and only when this has been demonstrated does the doctor feel that he has grasped the diagnosis.

This approach has led to many of the successes of conventional medicine. Natural science has given doctors the ability to in-
tervene on a microscopic level. For example, they can administer
chemical substances which inhibit the thyroid's production of thyroxine or, conversely, synthesize thyroxine to give to patients who

have insufficient concentrations in their blood. The discovery of an association between bacteria and infections led to research into drugs that would destroy the chemical make-up of the bacteria while interfering very little, or not at all, with the chemistry of the human body. The consequent discovery of antibiotics gave doctors the power to fight infections, and antibiotics are now used whenever bacteria are thought to be involved in disease.

Such advances have been made possible by the discoveries of natural science and may be seen as fruits of the reductionist approach. Perhaps because of its successes, it is an approach which has tended to dominate all others, and has even prevailed in the way medicines are understood and manufactured. Before the twentieth century, medicines were mainly derived from plants but also from some minerals and metals. A herbal remedy would have been prepared as a tincture by standing a finely chopped plant in a mixture of alcohol and water for a set time, before filtering off an extract. By contrast, modern pharmacy isolates individual chemical substances from the original plant and purifies them, with the intention of making more powerful and predictable medicines. The chemical is then often copied or modified, and made artificially. In this way, pharmacy, too, has moved away from the whole organism, the plant, to a single chemical component.

If one looks at the whole range of applications of conventional medicine, it is clear that it has made possible all manner of life-saving interventions. It has also brought about an enormous number of improvements to people's lives, for example through the replacement of damaged joints. Anthroposophical doctors do not claim otherwise, and recognize the methods of conventional medicine as sometimes being appropriate. But the fact that anthroposophical medicine offers methods which go beyond treatment of only the physical body is particularly important because the sources of many illnesses lie in the non-physical human elements. This book shows how anthroposophical medicine extends the healing possibilities of conventional therapy, and also how it overcomes the one-sided approach of reductionism.

It is a mistake to assume that the results of observation of inorganic matter can adequately grasp the full nature of living things. The laws applying to the life element are quite different from those of the physical world. Therefore, it is not surprising that life itself is one of the non-physical dimensions conventional medicine fails to grasp. It is understood by modern science that organisms, such as people, use material substances to build their physical bodies, but the living element of a person can never be comprehended by examination of those material components.

It is necessary to look at how the body grows and matures to get a sense of the activity of the life element, or etheric body. On death, the physical body decays back into the earth — it becomes once again the raw materials which had been used to build it up. During life, there were etheric processes holding the materials together, organizing them into a highly complex body. This life element can never be understood by the methods of natural science because it is not a material thing. In fact, our understanding of the physical body itself is advanced through a knowledge of the spiritual elements. It then becomes clear that the physical element functions in close relationship with the spiritual elements, subserving the identity of the whole.

In addition to the concept of the life element, the second area introduced by anthroposophical medicine concerns our feelings, instinctual drives and inner sense of the world around us. Our own inner experiences, such as our feelings, are obvious to ourselves but we cannot observe another's feelings in the way we can see external nature. Therefore, they are not accessible to the techniques of natural science, which limits itself to the observable and measurable. This problem has led to the development of a number of approaches to understanding the inner life, or soul life. For example, the biophysical model looks exclusively for a physical and chemical basis for consciousness, by examining the physiology and biochemistry of the nervous system. Another approach, behaviourism, tries to identify external stimuli which could be responsible for the way humans and animals behave. Psychoanalysis concentrates on unconscious, instinctive urges which express themselves in feelings and thoughts. The existentialist, or phenomenological, approach highlights that aspect of the soul which strives to develop an understanding of the world and itself. And social psychiatry examines the role of the social environment in shaping the soul life.

Anthroposophical medicine acknowledges that these approaches attempt to come to grips with particular aspects of the soul life, but considers that each one fails to describe it in its totality. For example, it is not possible to gain an understanding of the soul while regarding it as merely an expression of physiological processes. The soul world is a realm in its own right and the soul inhabits this realm, just as the physical body exists in the physical world. But this does not mean people's souls are completely separate from their physical bodies. There is a constant connection during life and the soul is deeply affected by the sensations received via the physical body.

The inorganic, physical element is common to humans, animals, plants and minerals. The life element is common to humans, animals and plants. The soul element — characterized by feelings, passions, instincts and consciousness — is common to humans and animals. In addition to these, there is a fourth element that makes us human and separates us from the other three kingdoms. It is a spiritual core which enables us not only to be conscious, but to *know* that we are conscious. In other words, to be self-conscious, or self-aware, beings. That we are self-aware is demonstrated every time we use the word *I* to refer to ourselves. This is only possible if we are aware of our existence as individuals.

The third area anthroposophical medicine adds to contemporary medical practice concerns this innermost sense of identity — the *I*, or ego. While our thoughts and feelings change from one day to the next, we retain a constant sense of identity throughout. Our physical bodies also change dramatically over a lifetime The material constituents are constantly being replaced such that, after a number of years, it is unlikely there are many atoms left that were in the body at the beginning of the period. Still, there is a centre we call *I*, which we experience as constant throughout. This inner identity distinguishes us from the outer world and drives us to seek for true knowledge of ourselves and our surroundings, beyond simply fulfilling the physical body's needs. Like animals, humans respond to external events, but only humans are able to conceive and carry out creative acts which go beyond instinct. This centre, this *I*, is the human spirit, and makes each of us unique.[3]

Realm	Quality	Kingdom of nature	Human Element
Spirit	Self-consciousness	Human	Ego
Soul	Consciousness	Animal	Astral body
Life	Life	Plant	Etheric body
Material	Weighable and measurable	Mineral	Physical Body

Figure 1.

A medicine to treat the whole person must be based on knowledge of all four aspects of the human being — the physical, life and soul elements, and the spirit. Each aspect interacts with the others but the whole person cannot be reduced to any one of them. Anthroposophical medicine describes the nature of these aspects and also explains how disturbances in their interrelationships can bring about illness. Conventional doctors know that a patient's emotional state can be the cause of certain physical illnesses, but they understand very little of how this comes about. It is particularly here, in describing how disturbances in the soul life can be expressed as physical symptoms, that anthroposophical medicine is able to offer valuable new forms of treatment. It aims to treat the causes of such illnesses, rather than simply suppressing their symptoms.

Any treatment which affects one element of the patient may also affect the others. For example, a conventional drug treatment aimed at relieving certain bodily symptoms may have its first effect on the physical body, but then go on to affect the spiritual elements. This secondary effect may not be beneficial. On the other hand, homeopathic medicines — which do not have such a direct chemical effect on the body but tend to stimulate the healing process — can be understood to have their primary action within the life element itself. For this reason, homeopathic medicines and their effects cannot be understood in terms of the measurable laws of natural science. They work on the whole patient via the non-physical life element and can only be understood in terms of the laws applying there.

In addition to remedies which work via the life element, anthroposophical medicine uses a range of artistic therapies which work primarily through the soul element of the patient. Also, through counselling, patients may gain new insights about their lives which lead them to resolve to make beneficial changes to their lifestyles. In this way, the doctor works directly with the patient's spirit, or conscious self.

Of course, anthroposophical medicine does not reject the use of surgery or conventional drugs when appropriate, such as in emergencies. But the spiritual as well as the physical consequences of their use have to be appreciated. Anthroposophical medicine adds to these methods a new range of medicines and therapies which extend the scope of treatment in accordance with its comprehensive picture of the human being. They are not just older, traditional forms of homeopathic or herbal medicine transplanted into the present on the basis that they may work. They are extensions of contemporary medical practice, developed on the basis of a new spiritual scientific understanding which adds enormously to what has been learned through natural science.

2. A New Study of Life

The life element, or etheric body, consists of formative forces which govern the organization of the physical body. Left to themselves, the materials that make up the physical body would disintegrate, as happens after death, when the physical body is left under the influence of the laws of the physical world alone. From a purely physical and chemical point of view, there is little difference between the body a moment before and a moment after death. But as soon as the etheric body departs, the physical body starts to decay from a highly organized structure into dust.

Every part of the physical body has a corresponding etheric part underlying it. The etheric body is not only responsible for building the physical parts into a complex whole: it also maintains them, constantly repairing and restructuring them. It strives to keep us in good health and is the source of our natural tendency to recover from less serious ailments in time, whether we see a doctor or not. This self-healing does not happen by chance. It is the result of the etheric body's constant opposition to death and decay in the physical body.

The etheric body is non-physical, so it obviously cannot be understood by examination of the physical body. Looking at the material parts reveals the physical body's form, which is an expression of the etheric body, but not the life element itself. Without an understanding of the etheric body, it is impossible to fully comprehend any organism and its diseases. This can be clearly illustrated using the example of cancer.

Cancer is traditionally understood to be a disease of cells. In a healthy organism, growth comes about through cell reproduction, and development through groups of cells taking on different forms, often of increasing complexity, whereby the different organs and tissues are formed. A fully developed organism contains many types of cells which differ from each other, and from the cells from which they originated. Cancerous tumours, which tend to spread and recur after removal, are made up of cells which multiply far more rapidly than most normal cells. As they grow, they tend to break through the boundaries of the diseased tissues, and even travel around the body via the bloodstream. The cancerous cells often become less differentiated than the normal cells in the affected tissues, as if the cancer had reversed the natural process of differentiation. In general, the less differentiated the cancerous cells are, the more malignant their behaviour.

Conventional treatment, based on this picture, attempts to remove the cancerous cells by surgery, or otherwise to kill them using radiation or cell poisons which, it is hoped, will do only minimal damage to the normal cells. Unfortunately, the chemistry of cancerous cells differs little from that of normal cells — unlike bacteria, which are easily targeted using antibiotics because of significant differences from human cells. A primary characteristic of the cancerous cells is that they tend to reproduce more rapidly than normal cells, so poisons are used which attack the most rapidly dividing cells. But healthy cells that normally reproduce rapidly, such as those in bone marrow (which reproduce to form white blood cells, the component of blood that fights infections) are also poisoned by these medicines.

From the anthroposophical point of view, a kind of template works through the etheric body which guides the cells as they reproduce and differentiate into the groups that make up the different parts of the body. Only through an understanding of how this formative principle is involved in bodily development, from the fertilized egg onwards, can cancer itself be comprehended. It then becomes clear that the cancer arises from a local breakdown in the etheric body, through which the human form is imprinted on the cells. This breakdown allows the cells to reproduce in an uncontrolled way and ultimately to damage the rest of the organism. Therefore, a more appropriate therapy for cancer would be one which helped to restore the formative forces in the area where the cancer had arisen. The forces to be strengthened would obviously have to be those concerned with maintaining the form of the tissues, rather than the forces of cellular vitality. This implies quite different treatment from attempts to kill off the cancerous cells.[1]

It is worth noting that some conventional doctors do not wholly embrace the conventional picture of cancer and have come remarkably close to the anthroposophical view through their own observations and reasoning. Professor David Smithers questioned the conventional view when he was Professor of Radiotherapy at London University in the 1960s. He said that if cells were studied in isolation by, for example, observing single-celled organisms like amoebas, it was apparent that they reproduced as rapidly as their food supplies allowed. They did not limit their own division or movement and, as they divided, the progeny closely resembled their parent cells — they did not differentiate into new types of cells. One could say they remained primitive. Professor Smithers pointed out that this was very similar to the behaviour of cancerous cells — they also reproduced rapidly, moved freely and did not differentiate. So it could be said that, from a cellular point of view, the cancerous cells were the ones that behaved normally.

Pursuing this idea, Smithers wondered why the cells of the body behaved in an apparently unnatural way during embryonic development. Succeeding generations became quite different from their parents and allowed their reproduction to be limited, as if they were subserving some greater function than their inherent tendencies. He thought there had to be forces which guided the cells to develop in such a way that the form of a particular organism arose, and concluded that the given form was the result of 'immaterial controlling forces without which no living organism can exist.' [2]

While natural science attempts to understand living things by studying ever smaller parts — from organs down to molecules and beyond — one fact to have emerged from these studies is that the smaller parts are in a constant state of change. Even the constituents of the skeleton, which appears to be the most permanent part of the body, are continuously changing. The mineral components of the bones are crystals of calcium carbonate and calcium phosphate, and even these hard substances are constantly dissolved and reformed by cells called osteoclasts and osteoblasts. This repeated cycle of change is true of the whole body, with the possible exception of the hardest substance of all, the enamel of the teeth. If we could tag all the molecules in a person's body, we would find that practically every one had been replaced a few years later — even, in some cases, a few hours later. Clearly, the essential nature of an organism is not its material constituents.

The nearest we can get to a realistic physical image of an organism is not a machine but, rather, a moving liquid form such as a river. Looking at the overall form of the river, we can see that it is to some extent stable, at least over a period of weeks. Yet, if we focus on the water itself, and analyse it into drops or molecules, it is immediately clear that these are flowing down the river and are constantly replaced. The contents of the river change all the time, while the overall form remains fairly constant. To take the analogy further, we also know that what determines the form of the river is not the water itself but the influence of the terrain over which it flows.

To search for an understanding of the human form in the body's constantly changing material constituents is as fruitless as it would be to try to understand the river's form by analysing the water molecules. In the case of the river, we could look at the terrain for an explanation, but natural science is of no help in discovering the source of the human form because we cannot perceive the etheric body using our physical senses. However, we could perhaps try to picture it by looking at cases in the physical world where an invisible force imposes forms on material substances.

For example, in the presence of a magnetic field, iron filings are arranged into striking patterns. The patterns cannot be understood simply by looking at the filings themselves. It is only by analysing the nature of the magnetic field that the behaviour of the filings becomes clear. There would appear to be some similarities here with the relationship between the etheric and physical bodies. But the etheric forces still differ markedly from magnetism in that they are not measurable or demonstrable using the techniques of natural science. They are spiritual, not physical, forces. Another approach is needed — one which can lead to direct conscious experience of the etheric realm, in the same way that we are normally directly conscious of the physical world.

In the eighteenth century, the German writer and scientist, Johann Wolfgang von Goethe, said that the life element in plants, animals and humans could not be grasped through what could be directly perceived with the physical senses. He said the real plant was not what could be seen at any given moment in its life cycle — a seed, a seedling, a growing green plant, a flowering plant, a fruit-bearing plant or a withering plant. Its true nature encompassed all of these, but was an invisible archetype which expressed itself in the various physical forms. It was possible to see a momentary manifestation of the plant, but not the archetype itself. Goethe further stated that, while the life element was not visible to the physical senses, it could be grasped in thought, and it was possible for the power of human thinking and reasoning to be transformed into a perceptive faculty. Thinking could be so strengthened that it became another organ of perception, through which the processes of life could be directly perceived.

Rudolf Steiner had this faculty — he was able to be fully conscious in both the physical and spiritual worlds — and was the first to express it with scientific clarity. Though people were normally aware of only the physical world, he said, everyone had the potential to develop consciousness that extended to the spiritual realm.[3] It was not only our physical form that had changed with human evolution, but also our level of consciousness. Such changes had happened throughout history and the time had arrived, he said, when the development of spiritual consciousness was beginning to be possible.

Steiner established spiritual science as a means of coming to know the spiritual realm as well as we know the physical world through natural science.[4] He described how spiritual perceptions could be at least as vivid as ordinary sense perceptions and, through training, just as reliable. They simply revealed another aspect of existence, as if a veil had been drawn away, rather as an extra dimension would be added to the perception of a blind person by the gift of sight. Consciousness of the etheric realm enables direct perception of the etheric body, just as the physical body is directly perceived with normal consciousness. In the same way that the physical body might be described as a collection of differentiated physical matter residing in the physical world, the etheric body constitutes a specialized organization of etheric nature inhabiting the etheric world.

The etheric body is particularly active during the embryonic stage of development, when the human form arises out of a plate of cells called the embryonic disc. It is also particularly active in the processes of nutrition, in which food is used for both growth and continual renewal of the physical body. This constant up-building quality of the etheric body is most dramatically expressed in plants which, in conjunction with sunlight, transform water and carbon dioxide into the sugars without which none of the other substances of living organisms could be created. The physical bodies of plants are thus the primary source of nutrition for human and animal life.

The laws of the etheric world are in many ways the inverse of those applying in the physical. For example, physics describes gravitational fields in terms of forces which emanate from points and radiate in all directions towards an infinite periphery. But, while they radiate out from a point, their effect is to pull objects in towards the centre. The etheric world is characterized by forces which emanate from the periphery and radiate in towards a point, while their effect is from the point back to the periphery.[5] This opposite direction of action of etheric forces can be seen in the physical world when, for example, plants oppose gravity by growing up out of the soil towards the sunlight.

The nature of the etheric world is such that it can only be described in physical terminology as infinite space. The etheric body originates in this boundless realm but, when it connects with the physical body at conception, it takes on a bounded quality which relates to the finite nature of the physical world. Goethe described this finite quality as a limited store of creative potential. If organisms had a 'limited budget' of 'creative capital,' as he put it, what was used up in the development of a particular specialization was no longer available for other creative possibilities. He cited as an example his observation that some animals had horns or antlers, while others had large canine teeth. He thought they could develop one or the other but not both. This is not strictly true — as Figure 2 overleaf shows, a number of species do have both. But, on closer examination, it can be seen that the larger the antlers, the smaller the canine teeth and vice versa, in an approximately inverse relationship.

Figure 2. Relative sizes of the canines and antlers of the male a) musk deer b) Chinese water deer c) tufted deer d) muntjac e) hog deer f) red deer g) moose. Illustration reproduced from Man and Mammals by Wolfgang Schad.

This suggests that Goethe was correct to assume that a relationship existed between canine teeth and antlers, but that it is
more subtle than he thought. This principle, known as biological
compensation, also shows itself in some of the problems associated with breeding animals. Usually, whenever a particular quality is achieved through breeding, other desirable qualities are lost.
For example, cows bred to produce very high milk yields have
been found to be far more vulnerable to disease and to require
more frequent courses of antibiotics.

The principle of biological compensation can also be applied to
the various parts of a single organism, including the human body.
If we look at the highly developed frontal part of the brain, the
two large cerebral hemispheres with which our thinking is associated, we see an example of advanced physical development. If
we look at other parts of the body, however, we see evidence of
retardation. From the embryological, developmental point of
view, the limbs (particularly the arms and hands) are structurally
very primitive and correspond to an early stage of development.
If we compare the human arm and hand with the front limb of a
horse or dog, we find that, quite early on, horse and dog embryos
go through a stage when their limbs have five radiating ap-
pendages, which correspond to the human hand and finger bones.
In the case of the horse, the central one of these develops exten-
sively, its bones fusing together to form the lower part of the leg
and hoof. In the dog, the bones corresponding to those in the
human palm of the hand form the lower leg, and its paw develops
from four of the five sets of bones corresponding to the human
fingers. If we ignore the functional value of the human hand for
the moment and consider it in purely structural terms, it is far
more primitive than the hoof and paw developments, which are
further specializations of the earlier embryonic stage. In terms of
morphology (the study of organic forms), the very high development of the human nervous system, and particularly the brain, is
compensated for by the relative retardation in the development of
the limbs.

The description of the human hand as primitive is valid in the
structural terms outlined above, but, of course, the hand is able to
perform a far greater number of different functions than hooves or

paws. The hoof and paw are structurally more highly developed but also more specialized, so they are less able to fulfil a diversity of requirements. Similarly, the forearm of a mole is superbly developed to function as a spade but this specialization makes the animal less able to do other things, such as run at great speed.

If we compare different parts of the same organism, it becomes apparent that, in general, there is not only a loss of versatility associated with specialized structural development but also a loss of regenerative ability. A comparison of cells from the nervous system with cells from a metabolic organ such as the liver, shows that the nerve cell is vastly more structurally developed, with up to a million dendrites (branches of the cell which connect to other nerve cells) and an axon (or nerve fibre), which can be more than a metre long. The polyhedral outer form of a relatively unstructured liver cell comes simply from the pressure of other liver cells, and the liver is itself shaped by the organs around it. Functionally, the nerve cell is highly specialized in transmitting and receiving the impulses which are the physical basis of sentience in humans and animals. But this corresponds to the nerve cell's inability to reproduce and a certain lack of adaptability — it is vulnerable to changes in concentration of either glucose or oxygen and is easily damaged or killed. By contrast, the liver cell is able to make a vast number of biochemical transformations, is capable of extensive reproduction and is very resistant to toxic substances, low glucose concentrations and low oxygen concentrations. Its reproductive capacity is so prolific that liver tissue can replace a large part of itself if removed, as opposed to the brain and nervous system which have extremely limited powers of regeneration.

The etheric body can be seen as a body of formative forces which builds up the physical body and supplies a rich but not limitless supply of creative potential. In less differentiated tissues, such as the metabolic and nutritive organs, the creative potential remains available for growth and regeneration. But in highly differentiated tissues such as the nervous system, once a certain degree of maturity has been reached, the capacity for growth and regeneration is limited and, in accordance with the principle of biological compensation, etheric forces are released to be used in some other way. They become forces of thought and mental energy serving the higher function of consciousness, and are then associated with the soul element rather than the life element.

The qualities of the etheric realm are in many ways the opposite of those of the physical world, where order degenerates into disorder. Wherever the etheric principle enters the physical world, it brings about order and form out of disorder and chaos. In the dead physical realm, it makes sense to gain an understanding of an object in terms of its constituent parts. Where physical matter is brought to life by the etheric body of a plant, animal or human, the parts of the organism are better understood in terms of their relationships within the whole.

3. The Soul

In addition to having physical and etheric bodies, humans and animals are conscious of the physical world and have inner experiences of instinctive drives. These characteristics are derived from the soul element, or astral body which, working through the etheric body, exerts a formative influence on physical development. This gives rise to internal organs, enclosed cavities within the body and other physical characteristics which distinguish humans and animals from plants. These physical differences may be clearly observed, but the most striking characteristic of the soul element, consciousness, can be more difficult to grasp. Through our consciousness of the physical world, we can be aware of pain when the physical body is damaged, but we are also aware of an inner pain when our feelings are hurt. Unlike the physical pain, these hurt feelings cannot be related to a particular area of the physical body, but they can be every bit as real and, in some circumstances, even harder to endure.

Anthroposophical doctors take the soul element, and the way it affects the physical and etheric bodies, as seriously as physical symptoms in understanding an illness and deciding on treatment. By contrast, conventional medicine has largely ignored it, concentrating instead on the physical body, even though the work of psychologists and psychiatrists has shown that emotional problems can play a substantial role in bringing about many physical illnesses. Consequently, modern doctors are ill-equipped to understand the soul element or to take it into account in treatment. Anthroposophical medicine offers a detailed picture of the relationship between the astral and physical bodies, and this is vital for an understanding of how the soul element can be involved in the causation and possible healing of physical illness.

Studying the soul element is made difficult by the fact that people experience their own thoughts and feelings first-hand, but others cannot perceive them directly. Apart from the anthroposophical view, several approaches to overcoming this problem have emerged within the fields of psychiatry and psychology. Perhaps the closest to conventional physical medicine is the biophysical approach to psychiatry, which aims to find the causes of emotional problems in changes in the physical body's biochemistry, in particular in the brain and nervous system. This approach has led to treatments such as electroconvulsive therapy and the use of antidepressant and sedative drugs.

Another approach — behaviourism — tries to identify external stimuli which could be responsible for how animals and humans behave. Through extensive animal experiments, theories of learning were developed which were used to interpret and modify human behaviour. Behavioural therapy can help patients with obsessional problems or certain mild forms of depression. By contrast, the Freudian approach is based on instincts and unconscious processes, which are thought to have a biological foundation but are nevertheless treated as psychological phenomena in their own right. This approach has led to treatment through psychoanalysis, in which the therapist interprets what patients express in a way that aims to help them understand what lies behind their behaviour.

A fourth approach, social psychiatry, emphasizes the effects of the social environment on the soul and looks at how social problems can lead to psychiatric illness. Finally, the existential, or phenomenological, approach analyses patients' experiences, their personality and how they make sense of the world. Patients are seen to be continually developing and maturing, and the term *self-actualization* is used to describe how they determine their own personalities, rather than being mere products of their physical and social environments or unconscious drives. Efforts have been made to integrate these different approaches to understanding the psyche, and most psychiatrists are prepared to use whichever method they think will be most useful for a particular patient.

Anthroposophical medicine recognizes that each approach contains an element of truth, but draws attention to the dangers of using any one method exclusively, as each one paints only a small part of the full picture. As one of the non-physical parts of a person, the soul element cannot be reduced to chemical or biological processes in the physical body. It is strongly coloured by the instincts, which have their roots in the unconscious physical and etheric bodies, and is also influenced by the higher element, the spirit, from which is derived a striving for a true understanding of the world and a need to find and fulfil aims in life that go beyond mere bodily needs. Anthroposophical medicine sees life as a process of soul and spiritual development, and crises in the soul, such as emotional problems, can therefore be seen as critical phases in a person's inner development.

The soul element is where consciousness arises, where feelings and thoughts reside. It is also where the impressions of the senses — for example, sight, hearing, smell, touch, taste, balance and temperature are experienced. The physical sense organs make it possible for us to perceive the physical world, but they are just the windows through which physical reality is revealed to the soul. For example, the eye is an instrument which is understood to receive visual images in a similar way to a camera. But it could no more make sense of the light patterns playing on the retina than a camera could understand the photographs it produces.

Contemporary natural science looks to the brain for this centre of consciousness and, certainly, all the electrochemical signals associated with the sense organs are transmitted to it. But there is nothing about the physical brain to make it any more capable of conscious experience of sight than the eyes. It, like them, is an organ consisting of a highly organized arrangement of cells, but neither the organ nor the cells are themselves conscious. The brain and sense organs are instruments of the soul, without which life in the physical world would be impossible.

There is a very fine balance in the relationship between the physical, etheric and astral bodies, and illness results from any breakdown in this balance. Finding where the root of the problem lies is a major part of the anthroposophical doctor's diagnosis. It cannot be assumed that the problem is to be found where the symptoms manifest: physical symptoms often result from disorders of the soul and the way the astral body influences the etheric and physical bodies.

This interplay between physical and psychological causes of illness has been explored by conventional medicine. In the 1940s and

1950s, a group of disorders began to be thought of as being caused by psychological factors, though nearly all of them involved changes in the structure of the physical body. They became known as *psychosomatic* disorders, and included gastric and duodenal ulcers, ulcerative colitis, asthma, rheumatoid arthritis, thyrotoxicosis (overactive thyroid gland), high blood pressure and eczema. Since then, there has been an increasing awareness that the majority of illnesses do not have a single cause, but result from a number of factors. As well as psychological effects, these may include hereditary predispositions, nutrition, reduced immunity, and contact with particular viruses or bacteria. It is now accepted by conventional medicine that psychological factors play an important role in bringing about both illnesses which involve structural changes (such as heart attacks, infections, diabetes and cancer) and functional disorders (migraine, indigestion, irritable bowel syndrome, sciatica, stiff neck and lower back pain).

As a result of further study of the role of the psyche in illness, two broad psychological types were described. The Type A personality was thought to predispose to heart disease and was identified in people with very high competitive drives, who constantly felt under pressure and found it difficult to relax. Men with this type of personality were found to have twice the risk of a fatal heart attack than had men who were equally outwardly successful, but who were more relaxed and easy-going. The more relaxed nature was called the Type B personality. Even so, the personality type was still recognized to be only one of a number of factors which can predispose to a heart attack. Others include smoking, being overweight, heredity and high blood pressure. Other studies suggested that an inability to express anger increased the likelihood of breast cancer in women under fifty and lung cancer in men. Also, of patients who already had cancer, those who reacted with hopelessness and desperation were found to have a poorer prognosis than those with a fighting spirit.

Another link with psychological factors was found in the case of diabetes. It was only relatively recently discovered that psychological stress can increase the body's need for insulin, though it had long been known that diabetics receiving insulin had difficulty controlling their illness during emotional crises. Previously, it had been thought that they did not pay sufficient attention to their diet and treatment when under emotional strain. Also, it is thought that the onset of diabetes can be triggered by emotional traumas, particularly bereavement, loss and loneliness, though it is again recognized that there are also other factors.

As conventional medicine has come to recognize that habitual psychological attitudes and emotional crises play important parts in bringing about many, if not most, illnesses, attempts have been made to understand the causal relationship. Different people with the same problems react in different ways, so it has to be asked how the psychological factor might contribute to the development of a disorder before attempts can be made at treating these causes. Conventional medicine has discovered that processes in the nervous system influence the regulation of hormones via the pituitary gland, which is directly connected to the lower part of the brain. Also, it is known that branches of the nervous system extend into the thymus and spleen, where certain groups of white blood cells, the lymphocytes, develop. Furthermore, it is known that the nervous system is connected to the adrenal gland and that nervous stimulation thereby leads to increased secretion of adrenaline and corticosteroids, both of which are produced in greatly increased concentrations during severe emotional stress.

It is thought in conventional medicine that the answer to the question of how the psyche can bring about changes in the body's immune system might be found by furthering this knowledge of links between the central nervous system and the rest of the body. But, while these findings are interesting in themselves, this idea assumes that thoughts and feelings are contained within the brain or nervous system, rather than experienced by a non-physical soul which is served by the brain and nerves. Predictably, this line of research has had little success in the development of new treatments. Anthroposophical medicine, on the other hand, offers a description of how the soul works into, and affects, the physical and etheric bodies, both in health and as a cause of disease. It can offer therapies which have direct effects on the astral body and treat the true cause of an illness, rather than focusing on relieving the physical symptoms.

It has already been said that the etheric body is primarily involved

with building up the physical body and constantly working to keep
it healthy. The astral body, has, in a sense, an opposite effect. It has
a breaking-down, or catabolic, effect on the physical body, and
thereby imbues a constant tendency towards illness. This contrasting effect comes about because, whereas the etheric body is the
basis of life, the astral body is the seat of consciousness, and consciousness in the physical world is bought at the cost of breaking
down, or *burning*, physical matter.

One aspect of the destructive effect of the astral body is that
consciousness is always accompanied by the breaking down of
glucose in the nervous system. This can only happen with the aid
of oxygen and is rather like the burning of a flame. Although this
burning process takes place in all the cells of the body, the brain
and nervous system are the most sensitive, requiring a constant
supply of glucose and oxygen from the blood. It is well-known
that brain-death occurs within a few minutes if the supply is cut
off, whereas the tissues of the limbs, which burn glucose during
muscular activity, can survive for as long as an hour. This destructive process, brought about by the astral body, has a proper
place within the healthy physical body, as long as it is balanced
by the healing effect of the blood, brought about by the etheric
body. Any significant imbalance between these two opposing influences will result in illness.

As well as its destructive effect, the astral body can also work
in harmony with the etheric body in a forming capacity. It does so
particularly during embryonic development, by imposing a
human form on the pattern of growth as the etheric body builds
up the physical body. However, even this involves a polarity of action. For example, an etheric process produces a limb with a hand
'bud' of solid tissue, then digestive enzymes are made which, in
an astral process, break down or 'digest' tissue to introduce the
spaces between the fingers. The hand takes shape through an interplay of creative and destructive forces, through the growth and
digestion of tissue.

Similarly, in the digestion and assimilation of food, the astral
and etheric bodies work together but in opposing directions.
Digestive enzymes and acid are secreted in the stomach, and
break down the food into manageable components. Only when

the food has been sufficiently broken down is the etheric body able to use the components in its constant regeneration of the physical body. The acid and digestive enzymes would break down the lining of the stomach itself if there were not means of protection. A thick mucus is secreted from the lining, and the cells in the stomach wall are especially strongly linked together, preventing any of the juices penetrating through it. The cells are constantly replaced, ensuring that the destructive capability of the acid and enzymes is held in check.

If this equilibrium is lost, either through excessive juices or insufficient protection, the stomach lining is itself digested, producing a hole, or ulcer. The smell of cooking, or the thought of a meal, increases the secretions in the stomach, as do feelings of fear or anger, and these physical responses to psychological changes are well-known to conventional medicine. Doctors are aware that many patients who develop gastric ulcers have been under stress for long periods, often with chronic frustration, but have lacked the means of expressing their feelings. This results in chronic overproduction of acid and enzymes. An anthroposophical doctor would see this as a case of the destructive digestive effect, which is an expression of the astral body, having persistently overpowered the restorative processes of the etheric body. A gastric ulcer is all the more likely to occur if the patient also drinks alcohol excessively, damaging the stomach lining, or smokes, which may impair the healing process by interfering with the blood supply to the stomach wall.

This polarity between the upbuilding life processes and the destructive processes of consciousness goes hand-in-hand with the trade-off between specialization and vitality described in Chapter 2. Consciousness is associated with the brain, nervous system and sense organs, which centre on the head and upper body. The complexity and specialization of these organs is characterized by a relative dearth of vitality — the cells are unable to reproduce and are relatively less able to endure adverse conditions. In the lower part of the body are found the organs of reproduction, nutrition and regeneration. The relative simplicity of the cells in the liver or the lining of the stomach is complemented by their tremendous versatility and vitality.

To maintain the balance between the destructive and regenerative processes, there must be alternating times of consciousness and unconsciousness, in other words, wakefulness and sleep. It is common knowledge that sleep is essential for reinvigoration and to assist healing during illnesses and that, as the day progresses, tiredness increases. When we fall asleep, our astral bodies withdraw from our physical and etheric bodies to enable the regenerative processes to work unhindered. At different times of life, the balance between these processes varies. For example, in babyhood, the period of most rapid growth is accompanied by the most sleeping. The etheric processes predominate and there is a great capacity for healing. In old age, growth has long since ceased, the healing capacity is reduced, and periods of sleeping are generally much shorter.

If the daily rhythm of consciousness and reinvigoration is disturbed, the imbalances which result will manifest as disorders. If the disturbance becomes constant, these tend to develop into chronic ailments. Anxiety and fear cause increased bowel action, so diarrhoea can result from attacks of anxiety, as is well-known to many who have taken exams or given public performances. The pulse, breathing rate and blood pressure are also raised by anxiety or fear, muscular tension is increased and more acid is produced in the stomach. If prolonged periods of stress cause chronic anxiety in patients, symptoms more permanent than a short bout of diarrhoea might become apparent. One patient might complain of palpitations on becoming aware of an unusually rapid heartbeat, another of tinglings in the limbs as a result of constant excessive breathing. This overbreathing reduces the amount of carbon dioxide in the blood, low levels of which are connected with the feeling of 'pins and needles.'

If the anxiety persists, diarrhoea may become permanent, or alternate with constipation, with abdominal cramps and a bloated feeling, as if the bowel was swinging between overactivity and underactivity (irritable bowel syndrome). When increased muscular tension becomes permanent, it can lead to painful spasms, for example in the neck, and may contribute to an attack of lumbago or sciatica if combined with lifting something awkwardly.

In all these instances, the processes normally brought about for a short time by a strong soul impression begin to manifest more permanently in one or another organ. The astral body's activity is too strong: in a sense, it penetrates more deeply than is appropriate into the particular organ. In these examples, there is not yet a structural change in the physical body — the dyspepsia has not yet become an ulcer, the diarrhoea is not yet colitis — but in many illnesses, structural changes result from an intensification of the same process. Angina — a temporary chemical damage of the heart muscle caused by a lack of oxygen — might be followed by a heart attack, when permanent damage occurs. Frequent diarrhoea might be followed by ulcerative colitis, a chronic inflammation of the bowel lining which results in pain or discomfort and the passing of blood and mucus.

In the physical world, order tends to degenerate into disorder, and it is only the intervention of the etheric body which reverses this process, bringing order out of chaos. The astral body takes the physical development created by the life element to a higher level, introducing greater differentiation and specialization into the physical body. Some illnesses can be understood to arise when there is a breakdown in a particular region of this higher ordering, allowing the partial reestablishment of the physical tendency towards degeneration. Such illnesses include those involving the crystallization of substances which would normally be kept in constant movement and solution, as in the development of gallstones and kidney stones. A crystallization process might be healthily expressed in the bones as calcification but, following the laying down of fatty substances in the arteries (atheroma), it would bring about a hardening of the arteries (arteriosclerosis) which tends to increase with age. This leads to poor circulation, painful muscular cramps on exertion and, after some time, could result in a stroke, senility, angina or a heart attack.

In oedema — when water collects in the ankles and calves, causing swelling — we have another example of a physical principle dominating the life processes. In the physical world, water collects at the lowest point it can run to under the influence of gravity. Inside the body, it should be in constant circulation, with the etheric forces counteracting the effect of gravity. If this life process breaks down, the water behaves as it would in the outer world, causing oedema. It follows that, if excessive activity of the astral body leads to a breakdown of the etheric processes, an appropriate form of treatment would involve strengthening those etheric forces while at the same time bringing back into balance the excessive astral forces.

The contrast between the anabolic, or upbuilding, influence of the etheric body and the catabolic, or breaking-down, influence of the astral body can be seen in a comparison of animal and plant life. Plants have physical bodies and, as living things, also have etheric bodies. Animals have physical and etheric bodies and, as conscious creatures, also have astral bodies. A comparison therefore offers clear examples of the functional differences introduced by the addition of an astral body.

The special vitality of plants, which have the life element without the opposing processes of consciousness, is demonstrated by their ability to transform inorganic matter into living substance. Animals cannot do this, and are only able to live by eating plants or other animals which themselves eat plants. Generally speaking, plants take in carbon dioxide and build carbohydrates, a fundamental food for animal life. By contrast, animals burn up carbohydrates, using oxygen to do so, and give off carbon dioxide.[1]

It has been described how the interplay of growth and digestion of tissue forms the hand during embryonic development. If this process is compared with the way a plant develops a hand-shaped, or palmate, leaf, the absence of the astral body is again clear. In the plant, the finger shapes arise because of different rates of growth in the developing tissue. The areas of more rapid cell division form the extensions, with the spaces in between brought about by slower growth. In animal (and human) embryos, successive stages of development involve the breaking down of earlier structures so that new ones can be built. Plants lack this possibility of developing by subtracting tissue and can only add — developing by what might be called *positive* growth. They can still change their form — for example their early leaves (cotyledons) may have a quite different structure from the leaves that later unfold — but the cotyledons are not dissolved away and can be seen below, and next to, later leaves. If humans developed in the same way, baby arms would be retained below the adult arms!

Another example of the plant's inability to dissolve its growth is given by the tendency towards woodiness of higher plants which live for more than one or two years. Wood is dead conductive tissue, which the plant lays down each year and grows around, giving rise to the thickening tree trunk and the annual rings which can be seen if the trunk is sawn through. Bark is formed in a similar way but, in this case, the dead material is deposited on the outside of the living tissue.

In the animal kingdom, there is a great range of development of the soul. Without the higher faculty of perception relating to the soul realm, it is not possible to perceive an animal's inner life directly, but it is quite easy to see how much more aware a cat or a dog is than, say, a worm. This observation is supported by the greater complexity of the nervous system in vertebrates and mammals. However, it is not only the nervous systems that become more complex with higher development, but also the systems concerned with breathing and the circulation of blood or equivalent fluids. One of the main tasks of these systems is to transport oxygen to all the tissues of the body and remove carbon dioxide. The increasing complexity allows for higher rates of burning of sugars in the cells (cellular respiration) and, as a generalization, the higher the development of soul, the greater the rate of burning (metabolic rate). The highest metabolic rates are found in mammals and birds, which are able to maintain a constant inner temperature, irrespective of their environment (warm-bloodedness). This enables mammals and birds to make rapid and powerful muscular actions irrespective of the outside temperature, whereas the activity of cold-blooded animals depends on how warm a day it happens to be.

As well as a higher metabolic rate, the more developed soul brings with it an increased food requirement and a more complex digestion to cope with the food. The complexity of animals' gastro-intestinal tracts ranges from a simple beaker shape in sea anemones, which have one opening as both entrance and exit, to a tube open at both ends in worms, to the much more sophisticated digestions of mammals. Wherever the catabolic, or breaking-down, processes are found in the animal kingdom, they indicate the involvement of a soul. Generally, the more efficient the animals' physical bodies are at utilizing nutrients, the greater are their levels of sentience and responsiveness.

Much as there is an inverse relationship between specialization and vitality in single organs (*see* the principle of biological compensation in Chapter 2), there is a trade-off between increased awareness and lowered vitality in animals which may be seen in their powers of healing and regeneration. A damaged limb will heal in mammals, but a limb or tail which is removed cannot be regrown. The cold-blooded lizards, with their lower metabolic rates, are able to regrow their tails and, lower down the hierarchy, a worm can even regrow half of its body. Even simpler flatworms, or planarians, can be split down the middle and regrow into two complete organisms, which is more reminiscent of the regenerative powers of plants than animals. Indeed, the less developed the animal's soul, the more plant-like the qualities of growth and repair become.

The awakening effect of the soul can also be traced chemically in the nervous system. Much information has come to light within the last thirty years concerning, particularly, the neurotransmitter substances, which are released by one nerve cell and affect another. They are mainly amines, which are derived from, and closely related to, amino acids, the constituents of proteins. One of the main amines is noradrenaline Its effect is very similar to that of the hommone adrenaline, which is understood to be released into the blood following nervous stimulation of the adrenal gland. Both adrenaline and noradrenaline heighten alertness and awareness. The pulse and metabolic rate are raised, glycogen (the form in which the sugar, glucose, is stored) is broken down, and the concentration of sugar in the blood rises, allowing the cells to burn more glucose to provide more energy.

As well as bringing about heightened awareness, this process increases the body's catabolic rate, the rate at which it breaks down material. In recognition of this, amines which stimulate the catabolism are called catecholamines, and most antidepressant drugs work by indirectly increasing the level of catecholamines in the nervous system. A drug which is chemically very similar to catecholamines is amphetamine, also known as speed. It has a very powerful awakening effect, causing excessive astral activity and 'speeding' thinking. It also causes a feeling of elation, but its effects carry the danger of inducing mania and addiction.

Through increasing the speed of metabolism, it also leads to weight loss and, in children, to retardation of growth.

The three main groups of biological substances, which are at the same time the three main groups of foods, are carbohydrates (sugars and starches), oils and fats, and proteins. All three are found in both plants and animals. However, animal substance (meat) is particularly rich in protein, while plant substance (fruit and vegetables) is generally richer in carbohydrates. Bearing in mind the relatively high levels of awareness in animals and protein in meat, it is worth noting that the constituents of protein (amino acids) are chemically very closely related to the catecholamines which stimulate wakefulness.

Another kind of amine which is very closely related to the amino acids is histamine. It is involved in the release of acid and digestive enzymes into the stomach on the one hand, but also in inflammatory reactions on the other. In the former case, it plays a role in the breaking down of food so that it may be safely absorbed into the body. In the latter, it mobilizes inflammation, which has a vital role in fighting invasions of bacteria and other foreign bodies. The immune system is stimulated by the process of inflammation to activate phagocytic cells — white blood cells that 'eat' foreign organisms, destroying them by secreting their own digestive enzymes around them.

Acting through the etheric body, the astral body brings about the characteristic physical forms of humans and animals. During embryonic development, it introduces folding processes which give rise to internalized organs and enclosed cavities within the body, and which depart from the predominantly planar development typical of plant organs. These folding processes introduce the nervous and digestive systems into the previously flat embryonic disc.

The development of nervous and digestive systems illustrates the astral body's fundamental qualities. On the one hand, it makes possible conscious experience of both the outer world and an inner realm of feelings and drives. On the other, it enhances the catabolic processes in the body, as typified by the wide-ranging role of digestive enzymes.

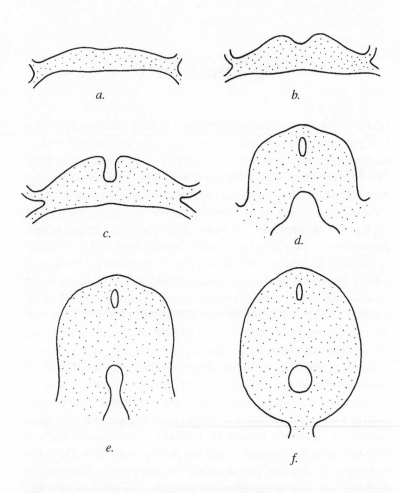

Figure 3. Sections through an embryo showing the early development of the central nervous system and, later, the digestive tract at a) 17 days b) 19 days c) 20 days d) 21 days e) 26 days and f) 28 days after conception.

4. The Spirit

Humans and animals are aware of the physical world and are able to experience pleasure and pain because they have astral bodies. However, there is an additional level of consciousness in humans that animals lack — self-consciousness. Humans are aware that they are independent conscious beings and, through this self-consciousness, are able to distinguish themselves from, and reflect on, the rest of the world. Thinking about the world brings with it the possibility of going beyond the animal's instinctive reactions to events. Humans are able to refrain from instinctive behaviour if their thoughts lead them to consider that it might be better to act in some other way. While animals act out of instinct modified by external conditioning, humans are able to form mental pictures of the consequences of their actions and other considerations, and allow these to influence their decisions.

Anthroposophical medicine describes this extra dimension of consciousness as the activity of the fourth element of the human, the spirit or ego. It is a person's inner core, the identity of the self around which thoughts and feelings come and go. The ego has a dual effect on the physical body. It works with the astral body in the breaking-down processes and also with the etheric body in the building-up, nutritive processes. It is particularly involved in thinking and, in that capacity, has a destructive effect within the physical body, particularly in the nervous system. It is also associated with the will, and the way volition is expressed through the physical body in movement — for example, the ability to stand upright and walk on two legs is a specifically human attribute.

The ego also bestows a sense of continuity and permanence from one hour, day or year to the next, which is made possible by the faculty of memory. Only humans have a true memory. When people wake up, they remember what happened the day before and what they intended to do on the new day. They remember who they are and where they live, and these retained concepts maintain a sense of identity. In animals, however, experiences come and go without being inwardly retained. Their external circumstances can trigger a kind of recollection of similar previous situations, but they have no power within themselves to recall events which are not mirrored in their immediate surroundings. Humans are able to recall past events at will, irrespective of their external circumstances.

People's ability to think for themselves — to the extent to which they use it — can free them from instinctive behaviour. In so far as freedom is achieved, it is the ego which makes it possible. Only humans have the choice between instinctive behaviour — essentially the pursuit of pleasure and avoidance of pain — and higher motives, such as concern for the well-being of others. The ability to choose cannot be separated from responsibility for the consequences of the chosen action. However, not only does the ego give people the ability to think for themselves, it also makes it possible for them to transform their own natures.

Some psychological schools acknowledge that freedom is a human characteristic. They generally see the childhood environment as a powerful influence, but assume that people are able to modify their behaviour through their awareness of what they learned when young. Thus, psychologies which include a theme of conscious self-development imply the existence of human freedom. Some go even further and introduce a concept of the spirit. For example, the existentialist, Victor Frankel, described the spirit as the part of a person that searched for, and could perceive, truth and meaning. The soul, he said, might be ill with a neurosis, such as severe depression, and yet the spirit may still be capable of perceiving a situation and grasping the truth. He described patients who endured considerable physical handicaps because of their illnesses, and knew they would die within a short time, who nevertheless used the last days of their lives to help other patients, some directly and others through the example of the way they bore their suffering.

Frankel said the doctor's role went beyond the care of body and soul, and included helping patients to find out what was meaningful for them in what they were going through. He quoted an aphorism from Goethe which he recommended as a maxim for psychotherapy: 'If we take people as they are, we make them worse. If we treat them as if they were what they ought to be, we help them to become what they are capable of becoming.'

By contrast, schools of thought which try to show how animal-like human behaviour is tend to deny the existence of human freedom. For example, in *The Naked Ape,* Desmond Morris makes the case that human behaviour which appears to be for the benefit of others is actually nothing more than a subtle refinement of instinctive drives, such as survival and sexuality. This reduces the human to the level of the animal and, if all actions are deemed to be derived from these urges, freedom and the spirit are denied.

Anthroposophical medicine sees true freedom as a goal which is being worked towards rather than a fully developed, bestowed privilege The ego, or spirit, acts as the agent of transformation in the process of personal development. It exists before birth and after death, and stimulates a departure from the straitjacket of learned, habitual and instinctive forms of behaviour, replacing them with free, conscious acts. This process of personal development is not limited to one lifetime. As has been seen, the physical body is constantly prone to decay, and remains alive only as long as it is maintained by the etheric body. When it dies, the spirit retains the developmental progress made in that lifetime and remains active in the spiritual world while preparing for the next incarnation.[1]

Through their thoughts and actions, people are constantly shaping the future of the world. The effects of their actions on those around them may be quite obvious, but it can take a long time for some consequences to be recognized. For example, only relatively recently has it become clear, particularly through an increased awareness of pollution, that our chosen way of life has had far more widespread effects on the world than we would have believed possible. Our individual responsibility for everything we have ever done is borne by the spirit, and survives death. Its effect on future lives follows a law which is described by a word borrowed from ancient Eastern teachings — karma. In future lives, our karma brings about opportunities for us to develop capacities that had been lacking and to redeem any malevolent influences we had brought into the world. However, we are not normally aware of our karma (unless we have undergone the inner strengthening process required for the development of higher faculties of perception) because if we were, we would cease to be free. The burden of responsibility would be so great, it would impose a course of action which would have to be followed as a predetermined destiny.

This idea of karma is not a concept of retribution, or of being rewarded and punished by a higher authority for good and bad deeds. Its description has been much simplified for the purposes of this book, but the principle that responsibility goes hand-in-hand with self-determination can be understood from examples in everyday life, without having to seek confirmation in the spiritual world. In general, children tend to have a limited awareness of the consequences of their actions and often behave selfishly and irresponsibly as a result. As they mature, they learn through experience how others are affected by their actions and tend to become more altruistic.

When we are preparing to incarnate, our karma influences when and where we are born, to whom, and the circumstances in which we will live. It shapes our constitutions and personalities, and provides the hard lessons in life, which hurt but also stimulate development. Awareness of this karmic element in our development opens up the possibility of finding a meaning underlying major events in our lives, such as illnesses. It becomes possible to see illnesses as more than unfortunate accidents — to see them instead as challenges which are both opportunities for and catalysts of personal development. This is, of course, very different from the contemporary view of the human as an advanced animal, who comes into being at conception and ceases to exist at death, and gives rise to a very different form of therapy.

From the anthroposophical doctor's point of view, the first step is to be aware of the possibility that an illness may have some significant meaning for the patient. By discussing the problem with the patient, the doctor might be able to help discover its meaning. What emerges may be quite mundane or very profound. A relatively mundane example might result from the experience of a short bout of flu or a flu-like illness. Although not very severe in patients in their twenties or thirties, it may be enough to bring it home to them that they have been exhausting themselves, perhaps through working too hard and by not maintaining a healthy balance of activity. They may decide that it is time to restore that balance and adjust their lives accordingly. There follow some more profound examples, taken from work at Park Attwood Clinic, an anthroposophical medical centre in England.[2]

A severe case concerned a man who placed very great value on his physical fitness and sporting achievements, and who developed a disabling arthritis. This forced him to re-examine his values and priorities. In time, he was able to find a new basis for his life but such a process, when forced upon a patient in this way, can be terribly traumatic; the patient requires a great deal of support while an adjustment to a new way of life is taking place.

A woman in her mid-thirties, who had put most of her energy into being a successful wife and mother, felt she could never live up to the standards she expected of herself, which were based on what she thought others expected of her. She became severely depressed and anxious, and was then incapable of running a home at all. This confirmed her feeling that she could not cope, and the depression and anxiety deepened in a vicious cycle. During this crisis, she needed a lot of support. For a while, she was given anthroposophical medicines and conventional sedatives, and was further supported by nursing and artistic therapy. The corner was turned when she began to let go of the expectations she had of herself. Gradually, she began to feel that she should accept herself for what she was, rather than measure herself against some arbitrarily imposed scale. This led to a feeling that she should act out of her own volition rather than her idea of what others expected and, by this time, the recovery was well in hand. After some months, she was able to resume her life with her family, and soon reported that she felt far more fulfilled as she had become more true to herself. Later, she said it had been worth suffering the pain of the illness for the transformation it had brought to her life.

A 52-year-old man suffered a sudden onset of severe eczema, which strong steroid treatment from his GP did little to alleviate. Outwardly, he was a rather tough character, who had tended to use his fists to sort out disputes. He was an expert teacher of karate and greatly enjoyed the martial arts. Out-patient treatment with anthroposophical medicines brought no obvious improvement, so he was admitted to Park Attwood. Initially, he continued to be aggressive and showed no empathy for patients suffering from depression, saying he could not imagine what depression was. He made it clear that he regarded talk of feelings as unmanly and not for him. The atmosphere of the centre he said he found strangely serene, and therefore unreal, and he was very derisory about the custom of saying grace before meals. He was started on painting therapy and therapeutic eurythmy (see Chapter 7), despite his protestations that it was a waste of time, and was given anthroposophical medicines and ointment to apply to the eczema.

The centre offers a very supportive social atmosphere, and there was plenty of time for him to talk to the staff, or co-workers, as they are called. After a while in this environment, he appeared to be softening slightly and, one day, in conversation with a nurse, he suddenly burst into tears when describing his experiences in the Korean War. He had never described these to anyone before and, by crying in front of the nurse, openly transgressed his taboo over feelings. It emerged that he had witnessed great cruelty and suffering in the war, and had been badly burned by napalm. He had never suffered from eczema before, and the areas now affected coincided exactly with where he had been burned thirty-four years earlier. It further emerged that he had been emotionally deprived as a child and had developed an aggressive show of strength by way of compensation. This adolescent way of behaving seemed to have been fixed in him by his experiences in the war, which he had been unable to deal with, and had remained ever since.

He attended a lecture at the centre about Leonardo's mural painting, *The Last Supper,* after which the depicted gestures of Christ and His disciples were discussed. The following night, he had a very moving dream in which he opened his arms to the position of Christ's in the mural, and felt as if energy was streaming from one arm to the other via the heart region. He woke up feeling certain that he would start to get better and, from then on, his eczema did improve steadily. He was by this time behaving quite differently, showing considerable sympathy and understanding for other patients, especially those with emotional problems. He also expressed a genuine respect for the work at the centre. His condition improved sufficiently for him to be discharged and, quite soon afterwards, he was able to return to work. It was clear that he had not only recovered from the eczema but had also undergone a considerable inner transformation. It seemed it was only through the acute and very uncomfortable illness that he was able to confront, and ultimately overcome, his facade of aggression and begin to express himself. The eczema had been a symptom of a deep emotional problem and had also played a part in a major step in his personal development.

In cases of illness in old age, when the patient is nearer to death, or perhaps suffering from a terminal disease, the significance may be more difficult to deduce because it may not be experienced fully until after death. It would be difficult to see how a terminal illness could have a positive meaning at all within the ideology of conventional medicine. However, anthroposophical doctors consider that there is still a meaning within the context of karma and personal development, but accept that its assessment has to be more tentative.

A woman in her mid-fifties developed symptoms of a very advanced cancer of the ovary. Her abdomen was markedly distended with fluid, as a result of the spreading of the tumour, and she died within three months of the discovery of the illness. Her life had been characterized by considerable disappointments. She had been brought up by her grandparents, because her own parents had had more children than they could cope with, and had always seen this as rejection by her parents. She was a gifted person, and was a qualified nurse and movement therapist. Though attractive, she had never married or had any children of her own, and this was also deeply disappointing to her. She never stayed very long in one place, though generally well-liked, and consequently had few close friends. In her forties, she had cared for her aged mother until her death and, during this time, had felt a degree of appreciation from her that she had not felt before. She inherited her mother's house and lived there alone, estranged from her brothers and sisters, who were all married with children.

During her cancer, which she knew was terminal, she was able to express some of her deep disappointments. Early on, there had been great fear and panic associated with the illness, made worse by the fact that the pressure from her swollen abdomen made breathing difficult. But she developed close ties with nurses and other co-workers at the centre and, after considerable outpourings of anger at the difficulties she had endured in her life, including the cancer itself, she came to a remarkable degree of acceptance and inner tranquillity. She died soon afterwards, but those caring for her felt that her chronic 'inner sores' had been healed before she had died, and that they would not be taken unresolved into the spiritual life after death. She had not only come to terms with her approaching death, but also with her life. In these examples, the illnesses enabled the patients to take significant steps in their personal development. Anthroposophical medicine aims to heal illness in a way which supports, rather than suppresses, such development. Through counselling, a deeper meaning to the experience of an illness may become apparent to both doctor and patient.

Now that the characteristics of the four human elements have been outlined, it is possible to see a more comprehensive picture of nature emerging. It can be seen that spiritual science is compatible with natural science, but adds another dimension to its concept of the world. In particular, the qualitative approach of spiritual science extends the quantitative parameters of natural science. For example, spiritual science identifies a qualitative relationship between the four human elements and the four natural elements — earth, water, air and fire. More specifically, it relates the human elements to the four fundamental states of matter or energy — solid, liquid, gas and warmth. By applying heat, the densest form of matter, a solid, can be made into a liquid. The heating makes the molecules of the solid more energetic until a threshold is passed when it 'melts' into liquid form. Similarly, a liquid can be made into a gas by applying heat. Warmth itself might be thought of as a *condition* of a solid, liquid or gas, which it is, but it can also exist in its own right, as radiant heat from the sun for example. In this sense, it is pure energy, rather than matter with more energetic molecules.

The physical body relates to the solid state, the etheric to the liquid, the astral to the gaseous and the ego to warmth. The relevance

Human Element	State	Natural Element
Ego	Warmth	Fire
Astral Body	Gas	Air
Etheric Body	Liquid	Water
Physical Body	Solid	Earth

Figure 4.

of this for anthroposophical medicine is that the ego expresses it-self in the physical world through warmth, the astral through gases and the etheric through liquids. When student doctors study anatomy, they dissect corpses that have been pickled for a year. This gives the impression that the body is a quite solid structure because the pickling turns soft, virtually fluid organs, like the liver, into fairly firm structures. The living body consists very largely of water and is, in fact, far more fluid than solid, the firmest parts being the bones. Gases are dissolved in the fluids and tissues of the body, as well as being present in the intestines and lungs, and the whole body is warm, with the deep tissues maintained at a mean temperature of about 37 degrees Celsius. In fact, closer examination reveals that some parts are warmer than others, and the temperatures of one organ and another, or different areas of skin can vary considerably. Using modern techniques of thermography, it is possible to produce a colourful image of the pattern of warmth of the skin. The *warmth body* can be imagined by picturing this kind of representation of the distribution of warmth throughout the body.

Looking at the apparently solid physical body gives the impression of a clear boundary between the person and the outside world. Everything inside the skin is seen as part of the person, everything outside it as part of the outer world. But this boundary is less clear when considering the *fluid body*. A certain amount of moisture is constantly excreted from the entire skin surface, which evaporates into the air. The boundary is still less clear in the case of the *gaseous body*, as there is a constant exchange of internal and external substances in the process of breathing. On breathing in, what had been outside is taken into the body via the lungs. Similarly, on breathing out, gases which had been dissolved in the blood become part of the outer air. The boundary is most diffuse in the case of bodily warmth, as there is a constant exchange of warmth with the environment.

Starting with relatively simple life forms, such as sea anemones and sponges living in salt water, it can be seen that the concentration of salts in them is close to that in the surrounding sea, and that they are very dependent on this level for their survival. They absorb oxygen dissolved in the water and give off dissolved carbon dioxide, and their temperatures are the same as the surrounding water. Slightly higher life forms, like worms, possess a rudimentary circulation which regulates the level of salts (solids) in the organism, allowing them to maintain a mineral content which is independent of their environment. However, their skin has to be kept moist so that they can absorb oxygen from the air. They remain dependent on external water, without which they would eventually die from dehydration.

Amphibians, like frogs and toads, also need moist skins to absorb oxygen, but they have lungs as well, making them somewhat less dependent on water (liquid) in their immediate environment. Reptiles, too, have lungs, indicating an internalization of the airy (gaseous) element. But amphibians and reptiles are cold-blooded: they are still dependent on the ambient temperature to determine their body temperatures. Apart from humans, only birds and mammals regulate their own temperatures, indicating an internalization of the warmth element.[3]

The independent warmth element acts as the physical medium through which the ego works into the body, creating self-awareness. The gaseous element (particularly oxygen) is the physical medium for astral activity in the body, which brings about consciousness. The etheric body depends on the liquid element (particularly water) in its work to maintain life. Without water, there is no life — only the inorganic mineral element, as in a desert. When a person dies, the bodily warmth is quickly lost, breathing ceases and the lungs collapse. Eventually, after the bodily organization has broken down and decomposition has taken place, all that is left is the mineral element, the skeleton.

While the element of warmth is the vehicle for the ego's physical activity, there are also many other characteristics of the presence of an ego. Self-consciousness, free-will, independent thinking, the ability to remember events at will and an upright posture have already been mentioned. The power of speech and the absence of fur or feathers (nakedness) might be added to the list. These are differences between human and animal forms as viewed at a given time, but there are also differences which become revealed when the life cycle is taken into account.

One distinguishing characteristic of humans is a very prolonged childhood. Most mammals also have periods of caring for their young, but they are always much shorter in relation to their lifespans. Another reflection of the presence of an ego can be seen in growth and development. The peak of an animal's physical growth coincides with reproductive maturity. However, in humans, growth continues after this point is reached in the early teens, and is not completed until the early twenties. Reproductive maturity can be seen as the coming of age of the astral body, or animal principle, but the coming of age of the ego, or human principle, comes later, at about twenty-one.

5. The Two Main Types of Illness

It has been seen how spiritual science, or anthroposophy, extends the view of the human being from a purely physical organism to a broader picture including life, soul and spiritual elements. In the anthroposophical picture, there is a delicate balance between the processes producing consciousness, which have a destructive effect on the physical body, and the upbuilding, regenerative processes of the life element. It is unhealthy for either the destructive or the upbuilding processes to predominate, and illness can result. Typical symptoms can be identified which characterize overactivity of the catabolic or anabolic processes but, before elaborating on this, it is necessary to delve a little deeper into anthroposophical physiology.

In conventional medical studies, the human organism is differentiated into a number of systems, such as the nervous system, the circulation and the respiratory system. Anthroposophical medicine describes three main systems, which are characterized by the way the three non-material elements of the human work into the physical body. The nerve-sense system includes the activity of all the nerves, the brain, the spinal cord and the sense organs. The metabolic-limb system includes the assimilation of nourishment, the metabolism and the activity of the limbs. The third, the rhythmic system, includes the breathing and the pulse.

The nerve-sense system is obviously concentrated in the head, where the brain and most of the sense organs are to be found, and radiates throughout the body from there. It has already been seen that the nerve-sense system is associated with consciousness, catabolic processes, lowered vitality and more highly specialized bodily structures. Where these characteristics are observed, the spirit has a destructive effect on the body whereas, in the unconscious, restorative processes, the spirit works harmoniously through the astral, etheric and physical bodies. The most sophisticated structures in the body are to be found in the nerve-sense system — for example, the three tiny bones that link the eardrum to the inner ear which are so delicate they can transmit the minutest movements of the eardrum. A similar microscopic complexity can be found in the structure of the eye. The low capacity for regeneration of these organs goes hand-in-hand with a withdrawal of the etheric processes from them. In accordance with the principle of biological compensation, these etheric forces become available for other activity, and are transferred from their upbuilding activity to the activity of thinking.

The structures of the sense organs come closer than any others in the body to the inorganic, purely physical element, almost as if they were machines. Therefore, it is easy to see how these organs lend themselves to comparison with man-made instruments. The pupil, lens and retina of the eye may be compared directly with the aperture, lens and film of a camera; similarly, the hairs of the inner ear may be compared with the strings of a piano. Virtually the whole body is infused with blood, carried in minute capillaries so that it is in almost direct contact with the cells of the body, only separated by the thin capillary wall. But the inside of the eye is an exception. Although most of the eye wall is richly supplied with blood, the interior is filled with a transparent fluid. The cornea (the clear part in front of the pupil and iris) and the lens are completely without a blood supply. The oxygen and nourishment they need must be dissolved through the clear fluids of the eye. As they are cut off from the vitalizing effects of the blood, they are particularly vulnerable to damage or ageing as in a cataract, for example, when the lens becomes progressively more opaque. As well as in the sense organs, the fine sculpting effect associated with the nerve-sense system may also be seen in the remarkably complex shape of the skull. Its detailed structure contrasts with the relatively simple form of a limb bone.

The metabolic-limb system includes the stomach and intestines, in which food is broken down and absorbed into the blood and lymphatic systems. The blood then passes first to the liver, where many of the newly absorbed substances are taken into liver tissue. The liver cells change glucose and other simple sugars into glycogen, and in this form they can be stored until needed. Amino acids are transformed into the protein albumen, a fundamental component of the liquid part of the blood. As organic substances are digested, the specific qualities they held through having been part of a particular animal or vegetable are destroyed in stages until they have a 'neutral' or virtually lifeless quality.

It is the liver that starts the process of rebuilding them into components of the human body, with the stamp of the human organism. From the liver, they are carried to all other parts of the body via the bloodstream. Hence the process of nourishment can be seen as a flow, through the bloodstream, into almost all the cells of the body. This metabolic process is centred on the digestive organs and the liver, from where it radiates throughout the body. The metabolic-limb system also includes the limbs, which bring the body into movement. In the muscles of the limbs, which have rich blood supplies, many of the substances brought by the blood are transformed into the energy expended in movement. All muscular activity also generates warmth, which is distributed to the rest of the body via the blood.

In direct contrast to the nerve-sense system, the metabolic-limb system is characterized by unconsciousness. We are not aware of the upbuilding processes taking place within us unless something goes wrong and starts to cause pain. The exercising of the will through movement is also unconscious. The idea, for instance, to walk across a room occurs in our thinking but the walking itself follows unconsciously. If it were necessary to think out the required movements of all the different muscles involved in walking across the room, we would soon fall over! By observing our own inner experiences, it is possible to make a distinction between thinking of something we intend to do and actually doing it. For example, this may be quite apparent first thing in the morning, when there can be a considerable delay between deciding to get up and actually doing so. On beginning to rise, we can get an impression that the source of the movement is not the mind, which so rapidly conceived the idea, but some deeply unconscious part of the soul. This unconsciousness is a characteristic of both volition and the whole activity of the metabolic system.

Whereas the nerve-sense system connects us to the outer world through awareness, the metabolic-limb system connects us physically. Our legs, in particular, resist gravity and make us mobile. Our arms and hands enable us to work on our surroundings and to be creative in the world. Through the metabolic-limb system, physical substance is taken in as food and we are able to be active in the physical world. Through the nerve-sense system, our physical bodies are linked to the spiritual activity of consciousness, which senses the physical world but does not directly affect it. The metabolic-limb system has an upbuilding and warming effect on the body; the nerve-sense system has a breaking-down effect and its organs are characterized by relative coolness.

In the middle, between these two *poles* of the organism, is the rhythmic system, which is expressed in all the rhythms of the body but especially in breathing and the pulse. It is centred on the heart and lungs, and hence the thorax. While the nerve-sense system, or head pole, is associated with thinking and the metabolic pole with the will, the rhythmic system is particularly associated with feelings. The heart is traditionally seen as the seat of the feelings, and a physical expression of this may be observed in the immediate changes of breathing rate and pulse which are commonly experienced when emotions such as anger and fear arise.

Rhythm offers a means of mediating between opposites, for example in breathing in and breathing out, or in the cycle of sleeping and waking. Checking the regularity of a patient's bodily rhythms is an important part of diagnosis. Most obviously, the pulse is checked but light may also be thrown on the cause of an illness by disturbances in the sleep cycle, the menstrual cycle, or the regularity of bowel movements. In terms of consciousness, we are aware of our feelings but less so than our thoughts. There is a dreamy quality to them which falls between the sharp awareness of thoughts and the unconsciousness of volition.

The mediation between the two poles may also be seen anatomically. Whereas the head pole has the bone on the outside with the soft brain tissue within it, the metabolic pole has soft muscle tissue on the outside, arranged around the bone. In the chest, there is an alternation of bone and muscle on the outside (the rib-cage), becoming more open at the lower end, which encases various soft organs arranged around the spine. Thus both structural aspects of the poles are incorporated in the rhythmic system, where the extremes of the poles meet and merge.

The two poles meet where the bloodstream and the lungs come

together. The bloodstream is associated predominantly with the upbuilding, warm, metabolic processes, and the breathing, which has a cooling effect on the blood, more with the sensory processes. Breathing takes place through the head and, although it normally happens unconsciously, is more easy to regulate consciously than the pulse. The relative speed of the pulse (in an adult, typically about seventy-two beats per minute at rest), compared with the breathing rate (about eighteen breaths per minute), also reflects the contrast between the dynamic physical activity of the metabolic pole and the relative physical stillness of the head pole.

The maintenance of health is very much a matter of keeping the metabolic and nerve-sense processes in equilibrium. As the rhythmic system is particularly involved in maintaining this balance, it has a special role in healing. Throughout life there can be inherent tendencies towards predominant activity of one or the other pole without necessarily causing illness. For example, there is a gradual shift in emphasis between birth and death. The early months after birth are taken up with feeding, sleeping and growing, the baby's body is softer than in later life, and its pulse is more rapid than an adult's all typical characteristics of the metabolic pole. In old age

Bodily System	Inner Activity	Level of Awareness	Physical Effects
Nerve-sense	Thinking	Consciousness	Cooling Catabolic Hardening
Rythmic	Feeling	Dream-like	Balancing Mediating
Metabolic-limb	Volition	Unconscious	Warming Anabolic Softening

Figure 5.

there is a tendency to *drying up* — the skin loses its suppleness and
the hands and face become wizened. Old people generally sleep
and eat less than when they were younger, and there tends to be a
loss of mobility and increased vulnerability to cold. These are all
characteristics of the head pole.

There is also an emphasis on either nerve-sense or metabolic-
limb activity which is associated with constitution. People with
dominant nerve-sense systems tend to be thin, with a more angular
body, and to look older than their years. If the metabolic-limb system predominates, the tendency is towards a rounder shape, even
plumpness, and to look younger than they are. There may also be a
tendency to a relative emotional and intellectual immaturity. These
descriptions are of contrasting constitutional types, but there is no
implication that illness will develop unless the predominance of
one pole over the other becomes too extreme. If this happens, two
main forms of illness can arise which are specifically associated
with the two poles. An unhealthy excess of the activity of the metabolic-limb system is characterized by an increase in warmth and an
excess of fluid (swelling) — the essential features of fever and inflammation. An unhealthy excess of nerve-sense activity is characterized by a loss of fluid, excessive hardening, a loss of mobility
and flexibility, and a build-up of mineral deposits in the body.
These are the features of degenerative or sclerotic illnesses, such as
osteoarthritis or arteriosclerosis.

In anthroposophical medicine, these are the two main types of
illness-the feverish and inflammatory on the one hand, the degenerative and sclerotic on the other. However, to see any illness
as purely one or the other type is almost always an oversimplifi-
cation, and usually both tendencies are involved. Rheumatoid
arthritis, for example, begins with marked inflammation in the
joints and they may become red, swollen, painful and hot. As the
disease progresses over the years, degenerative tendencies appear,
such as chronically deformed joints. Tuberculosis, which is essentially an infectious inflammatory disease, also tends to last a
long time and leaves hardened tissue and scars in the lungs, which
are characteristic of sclerosis.

The symptoms of the common cold include excretion of mucus
from the sinuses, which are inflamed and red, with inflammation of

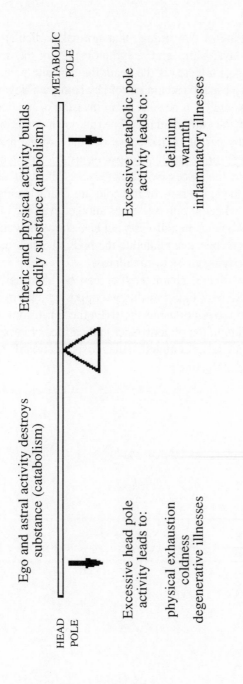

Ego and astral activity destroys
substance (catabolism)

Etheric and physical activity builds
bodily substance (anabolism)

HEAD
POLE

METABOLIC
POLE

Excessive head pole
activity leads to:

physical exhaustion
coldness
degenerative illnesses

Excessive metabolic pole
activity leads to:

delirium
warmth
inflammatory illnesses

Figure 6.

the throat and a higher temperature than normal, particularly in the first couple of days. Although the symptoms are of the metabolic type, the area most affected is the head, the opposite pole. People tend to be predisposed to catching a cold by being run-down or getting chilled. The chill can be seen as an invasion of the body by a foreign element, the outer coldness. The run-down condition, in an otherwise healthy person, is indicative of a lack of the restorative processes through too much 'head' work or insufficient sleep. Both the coolness and the 'excessive consciousness' are typical of the head pole, but the symptoms of the cold are characteristic of the metabolic pole. This not only serves as another example of the interplay of the two poles m a disease, but also shows how the physical symptoms can be more related to the body's healing processes than to the underlying cause of the illness.

In any given illness, characteristics can be identified of unhealthy overactivity of either of the two opposing systems. These are indicative of the relationships between the spirit, soul, life and physical elements in the patient. Such indications are essential if the doctor is to make as complete a diagnosis as possible and prescribe appropriate treatment.

6. The Use of Medicines

When an illness arises from an imbalance of the nerve-sense and metabolic-limb systems, a means of restoring balance is required to effect a cure. Anthroposophical medicine looks for examples in nature of similar life processes to those in the human organism, and uses animal, plant and mineral substances to make remedies. By contrast, conventional medicine looks at diseases in terms of molecular changes in the physical body, and isolates chemical drugs from substances occurring in nature.

All life consists of processes, such as growth, nutrition, digestion and respiration, which are physical expressions of the activity of the spiritual elements. Life cannot be regarded as a static state — it is created and constantly maintained by the dynamic activity involved in these processes. Consider, for example, a plant. What can be seen at any given time as the form of the plant is an organization of physical material which has been built up by the life processes within it. The process of photosynthesis, for example, when inorganic substances are brought to life with the aid of sunlight, is vital to the plant's ability to sustain itself and grow. Wherever life is present, such upbuilding (etheric) processes will be found; wherever consciousness is present, breaking-down (astral) processes will be found, such as the burning of sugars.

Conventional medicine analyses diseases in terms of molecular changes and develops chemical drugs aimed at counteracting the molecular changes to alleviate the physical symptoms. Anthroposophical medicine looks at the interplay of processes which cause the molecular changes associated with the symptoms. It aims to harness related processes in, say, plants within medicines which may then be used to stimulate a return to the proper balance of processes in the patient.

As plants have physical and etheric bodies, but not astral bodies with their destructive influence, they are particularly related to the regenerative, healing processes of the human etheric body. The plant's most characteristic organ is the leaf, which is where, in green plants, photosynthesis takes place. Leaves have flat, open forms and are typically located in the middle part of the plant, between the 'poles' of the roots and the flowers. Relatively high levels of organization and more complex forms can be seen in the flowers, whereas the roots tend to be relatively simple structures which have the *metabolic* role of absorbing nourishment for the whole plant.

In the plant, the flower is related to the animal kingdom, and the roots have a similar relationship to the mineral world. The flower demonstrates the greater complexity of form which is a characteristic normally associated with animals. Also, it is through the flower, with its colours and scent, that the plant relates to the animal world, for example when pollinated by bees. The roots, on the other hand, grow in the ground, and absorb minerals and water from the soil. The middle, or leafy, part of the plant is the most completely *plant-like,* demonstrating great vitality but less complex forms than the flowers.

The pinnacle of the plant's growth is the seed, which is one stage on from the flower. The seed itself tends to be a simple structure but it bears within it the potential for a whole new plant. This suggests a similarity to the ego, which is like the spiritual kernel, or seed, of the human, and contains the potential for the future development of the person. It can be seen from this very brief illustration that, in its form, the plant displays expressions of the mineral, plant, animal and human kingdoms in its roots, leaves, flowers and seeds respectively.

Although the plant does not have its own astral body, there is a slight penetration of astral forces into the flower, and this brings about its more complex form. In the flower, most plants just touch the astral, or animal, realm. But, in some, the astral element penetrates rather more deeply and this gives rise to poisonous substances within the plant, such as atropine in deadly nightshade. Just as the astral activity in the nervous system goes hand-in-hand with a destructive tendency, an equivalent astral activity in plants gives rise to substances which have a destructive effect if ingested by animals or humans. The poisonous plants have an *abnormal* level of astral activity, and this mirrors the state of illness in humans which is brought about by excessive activity of the nerve-sense pole.

In this way, it is possible to trace relationships between processes which give rise to certain substances in plants, and processes which bring about illnesses in people. Substances may then be identified which can be used as remedies. An important aid to this way of working is to study a plant in the context of its whole family, in order to discover the characteristics of that family. Not only do these characteristics reveal the expression of the family as a whole, but they also show which species are typical of the family and which manifest the more extreme characteristics. The latter can often be of medicinal value.

This technique differs greatly from conventional medicine, or allopathy, which generally aims to employ particular chemical substances to bring about a direct effect on the chemistry and functioning of the physical body. They are usually very direct effects, such as the use of steroids to suppress inflammation, or drugs to stimulate the production of insulin when this is considered to be lacking. The fundamental principle is to use drugs that cause the opposite effect to the symptom — if the illness involves what is considered to be too much inflammation, treatment is given to reduce the inflammation; if there is too little insulin, more is given or drugs are used to stimulate the body to produce more.

The principle of homeopathic medicine is the opposite of allopathy.[1] Here, the motto is 'like cures like.' Medicines are tested by giving them to healthy people and noting the symptoms produced. When a patient presents a set of symptoms to the doctor, a medicine is chosen which would produce the same symptoms in a healthy person. Homeopaths maintain that the medicine stimulates the body's own powers of self-healing, but it has to be said that homeopathy is based on many years of experience that it works in practice rather than on a detailed picture of exactly how it works.

The homeopathic way of preparing medicines also differs from conventional methods. A solution is generally made from whole plants or minerals and put through a process of dilution in steps, known as potentization. At each step, the solution is agitated, or succussed, before being again diluted. In a medicine which is specified as 6c (sixth centesimal), for example, the original tincture would have been diluted to one part per hundred, and succussed, six times over. It seems strange that the more the tincture is diluted, the more powerful the medicine becomes, but homeopaths have found this to be the case through many years of observation and experience of treatment.

The homeopathic doctor aims to select for the patient the medicine which has a symptom-picture most closely resembling the symptoms of the illness. To that end, the doctor is interested in aspects of the patient's mental state and general constitution which may be of little interest to a conventional physician. For example, it is useful to know if the symptoms are influenced by being warm or cold, or by any particular action or bodily function. In so far as the homeopath is concerned with a wealth of detail about the patient, and does not reduce the illness to a cellular cause, the approach may be termed holistic — the symptoms are related to the person as a whole, rather than being considered in isolation. However, homeopathy lacks an understanding of the causes of illness, of why a remedy has a particular symptom-picture, and of how the medicines actually work. Strictly speaking, it is not even necessary for the homeopath to know whether the remedy is from a plant or a mineral, let alone the specific nature of the plant or mineral, as long as the symptom-picture is known.

Herbal medicine offers another approach to the prescribing of medicines, based on the cumulative knowledge of hundreds of years of use of herbs as remedies. Generally, unpotentized preparations from the whole plant are used rather than specific chemicals, and herbalists often use the remedies to promote excretory functions, such as sweating, urination and the purging of the bowels, in the belief that these indirectly aid healing. The medicines offer many effective and gentler alternatives to conventional synthetic drugs and herbalists prefer to use these in most cases, reserving the more powerful drugs for occasions when they are essential. However, some herbalists have adopted the conventional, allopathic view of disease and seek to integrate the use of herbal medicines into conventional practice.

Anthroposophical medicine accepts that both the homeopathic and allopathic approaches are valid, and uses both potentized homeopathic medicines and unpotentized herbal medicines. It also recognizes the homeopath's and the medical herbalist's valuable observations of the effects of particular medicines. However, anthroposophical medicine aims to deepen the understanding of illness and medicinal substances by extending natural science with the understanding gained through spiritual science.

One plant that is used in the preparation of anthroposophical, homeopathic and herbal medicines, Aconitum napellus, provides a good example of how a qualitative anthroposophical understanding of a plant may be derived through studying it in the context of its family.[2] Aconitum, or monkshood, is a genus within the buttercup family *(Ranunculaceae)*. This family can be divided into three main groups: Thalictrinae containing clematis, actaeas and thalictrums; Adoninae containing ranunculi (buttercups), adonis and pulsatillas; and Helleborinae containing delphiniums, aquilegias and aconitums.

The Thalictrinae are generally woody climbing plants, or large plants with branching stems and many small, whitish flowers. The Helleborinae tend to have strong, straight flower stems, with single, or few, large coloured flowers. They have underground tubers or creeping stems and are often poisonous. The Adoninae are low to medium-sized plants, with branching stems and coloured flowers. If the formation and development of the leaves of all the plants within the family is examined, two distinct types emerge. In the first, particularly found in clematis, the leaves are divided into leaflets by stem-like structures, but these minor stems and leaflets still represent one leaf. In the second type, typical of aconitum, the leaves differentiate by developing deep incisions from the edge.

From wider anthroposophical studies of plants, it is known that the clematis leaf expresses a preponderance of development of the lower part of the plant, the root and stem. The aconitum leaf is more typical of the upper part of the plant in the sense that it has the appearance of having been eaten away as if by a similar astral activity to that which produces the fingers of the human hand (*see* Chapter 3). The Adoninae, the middle group of the family, may have either the clematis or aconitum types of leaves, or both characteristics combined, or neither.

Working from the stem upwards, flowers generally consist of a

THALICTRINAE	ADONINAE	HELLEBORINAE
Clematis	Ranunculi	Aconitums
Actaeas	Adonis	Delphiniums
Thalictrums	Pulsatillas	Aquilegias

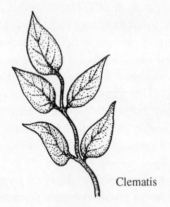

Clematis

Aconitum

Figure 7. Each clematis has three to four leaflets separated by stems. The leaves of aconitum are deeply incised.

ring of sepals, called the calyx, then a ring of petals, called the corolla. Within the petals there may be a ring of nectaries, which produce nectar, and within this the stamens, the male part of the flower. Within the stamens there is the pistil, the female part of the flower.

In Thalictrinae, and particularly clematis, there are generally no petals, just sepals, and a ring of stamens, which take on the display function of the corolla. In this case, the stamens take on the role normally performed by an organ found lower down the flower structure (i.e. nearer the stem). In Helleborinae, such as aconitum, petals are again lacking but, this time, the calyx takes on the display function of the corolla. Once again, we see in Helleborinae the opposite tendency to that expressed in Thalictrinae, with an organ from lower down the structure being, as it were, elevated to the function of a higher part. As might be expected, in the Adoninae several variations between the two forms may be found — adonis itself having real petals and sepals.

The upper parts of Thalictrinae are dominated by functions as-

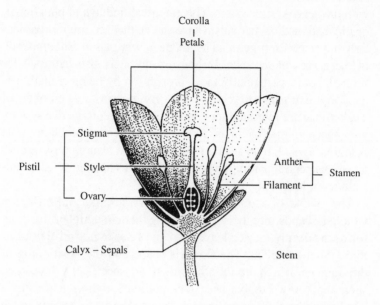

Figure 8. The parts of a flower.

sociated with the lower parts of the plants, while the reverse is true of Helleborinae. Expressed qualitatively, this means that Helleborinae tend to have stronger flower development, with the astral element extending beyond its normal province, and Thalictrinae tend to have stronger stem development. This picture is supported by the observation that Helleborinae have a preponderance of growth leading to flowering, or sexual reproduction (a higher and more animal-like process), while Thalictrinae have a preponderance of vegetative growth. Within the middle group (Adoninae), buttercups fall closest to Helleborinae and pulsatilla closest to Thalictrinae. The most extreme of the Thalictrinae is clematis; the most extreme of the Helleborinae is aconitum.

From this description, it might be expected that a destructive quality would be found in aconitum and, indeed, it is one of the most poisonous plants. The poison is distributed throughout the plant, but is concentrated and stored in its thick underground tubers. It might also be expected that aconitum would have a special relationship

with the nerve-sense system. The empirical findings of both homeopathy and medical herbalism have shown that aconitum is particularly indicated for trigeminal neuralgia, a very painful inflammation
of the nerves of the face. In homeopathy, it is also indicated for
feverish colds, particularly those brought on by being chilled, perhaps by exposure to cold wind. By contrast, a number of
Thalictrinae are indicated for conditions of the reproductive system,
with the extreme, clematis, used in male genital problems. The
Adoninae, which hold a central position in the plant family, also relate to the central part of the body, with adonis having its main indication as a heart remedy.

The picture of aconitum reveals a very strong astral influence
which descends into the sepals, raising them to a higher function,
forms the deeply incised leaves and gives rise to powerful poisons
throughout the plant. The flower's shape and the positioning of
the stamens (which produce the pollen) are specifically developed
such that only bumble-bees can pollinate them, indicating a
heightened level of specialization through the astral activity in the
flower.

The qualitative, comparative study of plant forms given above is
a greatly simplified version of the much more detailed investigation
which is required in practice, but it does give an idea of the way possible links with formative and spiritual processes in humans may be
discovered.[3] The study is pursued as far as possible before any con-
clusions are tested in clinical practice, and only if this brings confirmation are the links considered to have been demonstrated.

This emphasis on the study of processes, for example the
process which produces a toxic chemical in aconitum, contrasts
sharply with conventional medicine, which concentrates exclusively on the chemical itself. Anthroposophical medicine looks at
the particular qualities of the processes because, in so doing, it indirectly observes the spiritual activity behind the substances produced. The physical substances themselves are simply end
products of the processes, and can be seen as processes brought
to rest, or dynamic activity made static. Plant sugars (physical
substances) are end products of photosynthesis (a life process),
which takes carbon dioxide and water and transforms them into
substances which are characteristic of plant life.

Similarly, bark and wood are dead materials, but their source is the life processes of the plant of which they were once living elements. It is quite well-known that the source of coal, a mineral, is plant life, but it is not so widely appreciated that the thick layers of limestone which make up many mountains were formed from the calcium contained in tiny ancient animals. Their minute calcareous shells were deposited on the seabed when they died and, in time, became hardened into rock. Many minerals, which are rightly considered part of the inorganic realm, had their origins in living creatures. The transformation of carbon into various forms may be traced in its passage from the fluid organic activity of tree sap, to the hardened wood (when it is still part of the organism, though dead), to the fossilized fixed form of coal (when it has become completely mineralized). The study of substances in fixed forms (as in natural science) is the study of the dead end products of creative processes. If the life and soul elements are to be comprehended at all, the study of living things must be the study of the processes themselves.

Grinding a mineral substance into a powder and dissolving it — common steps in the preparation of medicines from mineral sources — can be seen as a kind of reversal of the process by which it came about. When dissolved, the substance is in a state more akin to its origin and can more easily be taken into the body as medicine, as all substances have to be dissolved in the breaking-down processes before being absorbed. If it also potentized, the chemical strength of the substance is reduced, but the spiritual process associated with its origin is enhanced. When a potentized medicine is given to a patient, the therapeutic effect of the spiritual process is taken in through the etheric body, the organization of life processes (whereas the remedial effects of artistic therapies are taken in through the soul and, in counselling, the ego is dealt with directly). The spiritual processes associated with the medicine can then have a harmonizing effect, restoring balance to the relative activities of the physical, etheric and astral bodies and ego.

In the human body, there are areas where hardening is healthy, such as in the bones, and areas where it is a symptom of disease or decay, as in the walls of the blood vessels. In old age, there is a calcification of the walls of the arteries (arteriosclerosis) and, at the same time, a loss of calcium from where it should be, in the bones (osteoporosis). A plant with formative processes which create a marked separation of the soft, fluid element and the hard, woody element is the silver birch. Its spring leaves display a delicate softness, while its bark is strongly mineralized, giving it a silvery appearance. The waterproof property of the bark, even when thin, made birch highly prized for canoe construction.

The soft young leaves can be used effectively in the treatment of arteriosclerosis when prepared as an infusion. Hence, to prepare the leaves for use against a hardening, mineralizing process, they are subjected to the opposite — to warming and dissolving in the preparation as an infusion. By contrast, the mineralized bark and wood can be used to treat inflammatory conditions and bowel problems when the motions are too fluid, as in diarrhoea. The hardening and forming qualities of the wood can be accentuated by turning it into charcoal (further mineralizing it) before preparing it as a medicine.

Like the birch leaves, a mixture of herbs called Menodoron, which is used to help regulate the menstrual cycle, is prepared by the warming process of cooking. Medicines prepared in this way are called decoctions, and the warming helps to prepare the medicine to act on the metabolic pole. Conversely, when aconite is prepared for the treatment of conditions of the nerve-sense system, cold processes are used, which help to prepare the medicine to act on the head pole.

The importance of warming is also seen when ethereal, or essential, oils from plants are prepared for medicinal application. Plants such as lavender, rosemary, thyme, sage, marjoram, peppermint and lemon balm all have aromatic, warming qualities. They often benefit people suffering from sclerotic (hardening) diseases through their warming effect. In anthroposophical medicine, they are given in potentized form by mouth or injection, but their most widespread use is applied to the skin as massage oil or finely dispersed in water in an oil bath.

The mode of thinking involved in the anthroposophical way of relating substances to disease processes differs markedly from that associated with modern chemistry and physics and, for this reason, it can prove difficult to grasp. It should be remembered that the links can be seen directly with spiritual perception but, lacking this, it is necessary to develop a discipline of thinking which is able to go beyond the limitations of natural science described earlier. This is not to belittle the considerable achievements of chemistry and physics, but these achievements should not be allowed to give the impression that the nature of substance may not be approached in any other way.

Modern scientists are justified in criticizing the inexactitudes of the alchemy of the Middle Ages, but it is fair to say that the alchemists were not so much engaged in early attempts at analytical chemistry as in discovering qualitative connections between the chemical elements and the human soul and spirit.[4] Modern chemistry regards substances as purely objects of the material world. That the alchemists had a quite different attitude is made clear by their religious reverence towards the substances they studied. While it would be inappropriate to return to the ways of the alchemists, it would be quite wrong to think of them as completely misguided because subsequent research has invalidated some of their work. Theirs was a qualitative approach to the study of matter, and a modern qualitative approach is needed to balance the one-sidedness of the quantitative approach of natural science. It is this qualitative aspect which is at work in the prescription of potentized medicines, as opposed to the techniques of conventional medicine, which tend to be too heavily based on evidence from the laboratory. For example, in conventional medicine, an antacid is given for indigestion. This simply uses an alkali to neutralize acid in the stomach, just as can be done in a test-tube in a laboratory experiment, but takes no account of what may be behind the symptom of the indigestion.

For the alchemists, there were three main chemical principles, represented by sulphur, mercury and salt. Sulphur is associated with the combustible, potentially volatile state; mercury with the fluid, mediating state; and salt with the crystalline, fixed state The combustible tendency of sulphur is related to the warming activity of the metabolic-limb system; the mediating tendency of mercury is related to the harmonizing activity of the rhythmic system; and the crystallizing tendency associated with salt is related to the hardening, sclerotic processes of the nerve-sense system.

A crystalline substance which particularly represents the salt principle is silica, which composes about ninety-five per cent of the earth's crust. It is present in small concentrations in the body, especially in the skin and hair. As the main constituent of glass, silica displays the quality of transparency, like the lens in the eye. It also fulfils a key role in modern communication and information technology in the form of silicon chips and fibre optics. These relationships can be pursued, but it can already be seen that, both within the body and in the external world, silica is associated with nerve-sense activity. It comes as no surprise then, to find that classical homeopathy regards silica as the prime remedy for treating weak, neurasthenic states, sensitivity to cold and susceptibility to overstimulation of the nervous system. In anthroposophical medicine, it is also used to treat a tendency to recurrent colds and sinusitis. These conditions all represent an excessive activity of the nerve-sense system.

Sulphur is itself a prime example of the sulphur principle. It is a vital component of proteins, the main structural element of human and animal bodies, and is essential for the building up of the body, a major task of the metabolic system. When life ceases, and decomposition of the organic material ensues, sulphur is one of the first elements to separate, which contributes to the characteristic smell of decomposition. In medicinal applications, sulphur stimulates the metabolic processes. For example, in an infection, if the inflammation threatens to become chronic, sulphur can be used to reactivate it and, thereby, bring the infection to a resolution. In conventional medicines sulphur is used as an ointment to soften the skin in treating conditions like acne.

Two remedies from the mineral kingdom which are very closely related from a conventional chemical point of view are calcium and magnesium. Calcium, which bridges the animal and mineral worlds, is a major constituent of animal shells and of human and animal bones. Magnesium, on the other hand, has a greater role in plant life. It is the central element in the chlorophyll molecule, which lies at the heart of the plant's ability to photosynthesize, and thus transform inorganic material into living tissue. This strong association with plants, and their ability to create organic substance, demonstrates its relationship to the etheric, upbuilding processes in humans. Magnesium can be used to treat both depressed vitality and emotional depression.

Calcium plays a central role in animal and human locomotion, not only as a component of bones but also because it is involved in muscular contraction. Its closer relationship to the astral body is also reflected in its ability to counteract overactive etheric processes in patients. In anthroposophical medicine, it is used to treat excessive inflammatory or allergic responses, and also overactive fluid tendencies, such as excessive growth in children, which is accompanied by overdevelopment of the lymphatic tissue of the neck and throat, and can predispose to chronic tonsillitis.

In anthroposophical practice, the doctor may use a remedy to counterbalance the illness process (the allopathic principle) or a remedy with qualities which match the tendencies of the illness (the homeopathic principle). Or a combination of substances may be prescribed which will work on the illness in different, complementary ways. For example, migraine headaches are thought to be caused by the blood vessels of the brain at first narrowing in spasm, then becoming dilated, with a seeping of fluid into the surrounding tissue. In coming to a qualitative understanding of such an illness, it may be noted that the problem involves a blood process (related to the metabolic system) in the brain (nerve-sense system). The initial symptom is a contraction and tightening (characteristic of the nerve-sense system), followed by an excessive dilation of the blood vessels (metabolic system).

In many cases, attacks follow periods of mental strain, which supports the idea that the cause lies in the nerve-sense system, but the end result is a predominance of the metabolic processes in the head — the centre of the nerve-sense system. This picture may be further complicated by the additional symptom of nausea, which can be regarded as a pathological consciousness in the metabolic region. In good health, the processes of the stomach are deeply unconscious — we are unaware of them until something goes wrong. The therapeutic aim is to reduce the excess of metabolic activity in the head and nerve-sense activity in the stomach. For this, an anthroposophical preparation called Bidor is used. It contains silica to harmonize the nerve-sense system, and sulphur combined with iron, which balances the metabolic and respiratory functions, alleviating the overflow of the metabolic processes into the head.

As all anthroposophical doctors are first trained in conventional medicines they are also able to prescribe conventional drugs when appropriate. Many of these drugs are extremely powerful and their use in emergencies can be very valuable, even life-saving. However, their equally powerful and damaging side effects are also becoming increasingly recognized, by both the public and conventional doctors. For example, steroids are known to cause osteoporosis (weakening of the bones) and adrenal problems, and some non-steroid anti-rheumatic drugs predispose to irritation and possible haemorrhage in the stomach. Less widely recognized are the more subtle and long-term effects, which may not show up until much later in life. Many conventional drugs suppress the symptoms of specific illnesses. For example, painkillers and anti-inflammatory drugs used to treat osteoarthritis can temporarily alleviate pain and reduce swelling, but it is becoming apparent that they have no positive effect on the long-term outcome of the illness, and may worsen its progression.

Antibiotics can be life-saving in very severe infections, but they are used by most GPs to treat a myriad of minor infections which would resolve themselves if given a little time. It is acknowledged by conventional medicine that this practice has led to strains of bacteria developing which are resistant to antibiotics, but the likelihood that indiscriminate use of antibiotics reduces the body's own ability to fight infections has been overlooked. The main cause of most infections is the patient's susceptibility to them, rather than the mere presence of the bacteria or virus. While the use of antibiotics shortens the period of infection by killing the offending bacteria, it does nothing for the patient's susceptibility to infection. Anthroposophical medicine offers a wide range of preparations which stimulate and enhance the body's own healing response rather than killing off the foreign elements for it. Antibiotics can then be reserved for more serious infections, when they might be essential.

While anthroposophical doctors certainly do not claim that conventional medicines should not be used under any circumstances, and prescribe them when they feel their use is appropriate, they are aware of the one-sidedness of their effects and the problems which might result from their use. The need for conventional drugs can often be obviated by the use of anthroposophical medicines, sometimes to a remarkable degree. For example, at one anthroposophically orientated National Health Service general practice in England, the quantity of conventional medicines prescribed has been reduced to twenty-five per cent of what the average GP uses in a comparably sized practice. This has been achieved despite having the usual cross-section of patients found in any NHS surgery, and despite the fact that only a minority of the patients specifically chose the practice because of its anthroposophical orientation. Clearly, the principles of anthroposophical medicine have a major role to play, even within contemporary general practice.

7. Artistic Therapies

In modern society, art is commonly regarded as a luxury or optional extra, with science more highly valued, especially for its technical applications. In past societies, for example in the Middle Ages, religion and art were inseparable, and played much greater roles in people's lives. Painting, music, sculpture and architecture were considered to be sacred activities. The substance of the physical world is transformed in artistic creation in such a way that it takes on a special value for people. In this sense the development of the arts through the different cultural periods of history may be seen as a reflection of humanity's changing consciousness.

Different times have given rise to characteristic forms of expression — the harmonious proportions of Greek architecture and sculpture, the two-dimensional painting of the early Christian era, the first vivid expression of personality in the faces painted by Rembrandt, the formal structures of Classical music and the self-expression in the music of the Romantic period. Artistic activity also plays an important part in the further development of consciousness, for both the individual and society as a whole.

With a knowledge of how the four human elements are involved in artistic activity, it is possible to develop exercises which work in a specific way on those aspects of a patient. The emphasis in such exercises is on the effect on the patient rather than the final artistic creation, and this distinguishes artistic therapy from other artistic pursuits. The way particular artistic activities relate to the different human elements can be understood most readily in the cases of music, painting, sculpture and modelling. Lovers of music may well have had the feeling that something of a higher or spiritual nature is expressed in, for example, a symphony. And everyone will be aware of the powerful effect music has on the feelings. It can evoke profound moods of sadness or joy, and span the extremes of passion and pensiveness. This is one indication that, in music, the laws of the spirit express themselves in the realm of the soul — the human identity, the ego, is expressed in the realm of the astral body, the seat of feelings and emotions.

Painting is a manifestation of the laws of the astral body expressed in the etheric realm. Colours, like music, can evoke powerful feelings, for example through the beauty of a sunset, a landscape or a flower. Whereas music is expressed in time and sculpture in three-dimensional space, painting uses planar surfaces. Flat surfaces are particularly associated with the life element and the etheric realm. The main organs of the plant world, leaves, are roughly two-dimensional and, on the microscopic level, the primary organs for life processes are two-dimensional cell membranes. In painting, characteristics of the astral realm, colours are expressed in fluids on a two-dimensional surface, the medium of the etheric realm.

The principle of form in sculpture does not have the dramatic effect on our emotions that music or colour do, indicating that the astral body is not involved in the same way. The sculptor works physical material into the desired three-dimensional form just as the etheric body constantly builds up physical substances into a human form. In sculpture and modelling, the laws of the etheric body are expressed in the physical realm.

An art of movement called eurythmy was devised by Rudolf Steiner to express the forms of movement of the etheric body in the physical realm. This, too, has a therapeutic application when exercises are designed to work back into the patient's inner nature. The etheric movement can be seen physically in the way the tissues and fluids of an embryo extend and fold to build up the human body from what is initially a simple ball of cells. The etheric body is a medium for the expression of the ego and astral body as well as its own inherent movements, so the forms and gestures of eurythmy also relate to music and to the ways the sounds of speech are formed by the larynx, tongue, teeth and lips. In this way, the movements of eurythmy are able to be an expression of the whole human being through the medium of the physical body.

Anthroposophical medicine seeks to understand a patient's illness in terms of the interrelationships between the ego, astral

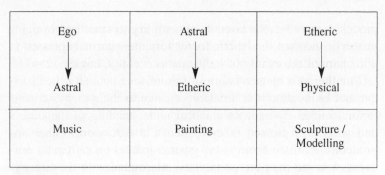

Ego → Astral	Astral → Etheric	Etheric → Physical
Music	Painting	Sculpture / Modelling

Figure 9.

body, etheric body and physical body. The therapeutic aim is to influence the activity of one or more of these elements in order to regain a healthy balance. As described above, the different arts arise through the interplay of two or more of these elements. By developing artistic activity that works back into the elements concerned, a therapeutic influence can be achieved. The value of a course of artistic therapy can be specific or general. It may support a specific bodily process but, in addition, the new experiences introduced by the therapy can strengthen self-confidence generally, and this can be helpful in both physical and psychiatric disorders. Also, it is often found that the process of overcoming artistic problems that arise during treatment produces indications and encouragement for the overcoming of fundamental problems in the patient's life and health.

The therapists, who are trained in both the art form and its therapeutic application, practise in close conjunction with anthroposophical doctors. Treatment is normally one-to-one but can also be in groups when necessary. Initial exercises reveal to the therapist the nature of any one-sided tendencies in the patient. Along with the medical picture described by the doctor, this helps the therapist to create a sequence of artistic exercises to meet the particular needs of the patient.

Sculpture or modelling therapy relates particularly to the working of the etheric body into the physical body, and is strongly indicated when the illness is expressed as a problem of forming. For example, in ulcerative colitis, the forming activity of the bowel is weakened. In psychiatric disorders, weakness in the form-giving processes may be expressed as an inability to structure thoughts properly or, when the etheric forces lose their normal connection with particular organs, in hallucinations (*see* Chapter 12). The artistic therapist creates a series of exercises to counter the disorder and bring about the necessary change in the patient's constitution, guided by both the medical understanding of the illness and what is expressed in the patient's artistic work. Other approaches to artistic therapy lay great emphasis on catharsis, self-expression and the psychoanalytical interpretation of the patient's creations. In anthroposophical artistic therapy, the emphasis is on stimulating and encouraging therapeutic effects in the patient's whole constitution.

One patient, whose diagnosis included a predominance of nerve-sense activity, began his modelling therapy by making numerous little cubes and stalactite shapes which were very intellectually thought-out. He was given the exercise of creating a large plane of clay containing wave forms as this encourages a greater affinity with the watery element and a less intellectual frame of mind. Another patient, who was just beginning to recover from acute schizophrenia, was still very anxious and was having difficulty concentrating. He was asked to fashion a sphere with his hands, then to form geometrical shapes such as a large cube. The forming aspect of this treatment helped his concentration and had a calming effect. These exercises should not be thought of as specific prescriptions, but as examples of tasks the therapists can give to patients as part of an individualized course of treatment. The course not only relates to the illness in question, but also to how it affects the patient's particular constitution and how that is expressed artistically.

In painting therapy, the qualities of light and colour are expressed via a watery medium. As air is the carrier of light, we can see how in watercolour painting the natural elements of air and water come together. Air and water are related to the astral and etheric bodies respectively, and the interplay between these bodies is central to the harmonious function of all four elements of the human being. In the physical body, the meeting of the airy and watery elements is most clearly expressed in the lungs, where breathed-in air interacts with the blood. Oxygen is dissolved into the blood from the air, while carbon dioxide is released from the blood and breathed out. This process takes place in the rhythmic system, which has a special relationship with feelings.

Painting therapy may be used to treat a wide range of physical and psychological disorders, and is particularly indicated for disorders of the rhythmic system, such as breathing problems. In asthma, for example, the rhythm of the breathing is impaired because the airways become partially blocked by an inflammatory process that causes swelling and an excessive build-up of fluid. The balance between the airy and watery elements has been lost and, in this case, the artistic therapist would look for ways to balance the predominance of etheric (watery) activity. Painting therapy can also be used to treat conditions characterized by excessive dryness and hardening, such as the sclerotic diseases, osteoarthritis and arteriosclerosis (hardening of the arteries). In psychiatric treatment, it can be used to treat such disorders as obsessional problems and depression *(see* Chapter 12).

In fact, very diverse possibilities for treatment are offered by painting therapy. The colours themselves have a therapeutic effect, such as the inherent qualities of warmth, activity and expansion in the reds, oranges and yellows, or the coolness, passivity and contraction of the blues and greens. Unconsciously, we are constantly affected by colours, and the therapist tries to work with these effects in the course of treatment. The polarities of light and dark or form and fantasy may also be used to good effect. Painting techniques offer further therapeutic opportunities, for example working on wet paper, which can stimulate spontaneity, or applying fine layers of colour to dry paper, which tends to encourage a quieter, more reflective mood. The activity of painting normally involves short periods of total involvement interspersed with moments of standing back to observe and reflect. In this way, it can be seen to mirror the rhythmic cycle of breathing — *breathing out* the creative activity and *breathing in* the quieter moments of observation.

Another form of artistic treatment, which stimulates an inner process through external activity, is eurythmy therapy. In modern life, people are often engaged in several activities at once, for example driving while listening to music and thinking about work.

The thoughts tend to be unrelated to the feelings created by the music, and the actions involved in driving the car tend to be unrelated to both. When the pressures of modern life cause thoughts, feelings and actions to be fragmented in this way, the soul activity also becomes fragmented. This leads to a poor union between the soul and the physical body which, in advanced cases, may manifest as disturbances in bodily movement as well as illness. Eurythmy treatment is particularly valuable in such illnesses when, for example, the posture may have become distorted, the gait unnaturally heavy or light, or the breathing shallow and unrhythmical. Eurythmy therapy aims to restore a healthy relationship between the soul and the physical body, and to correct any disturbances in movement. It also works towards a reunion of the patient's thoughts, feelings and actions.

The bodily movements or gestures which are used as exercises are related to the vowel and consonant sounds that are made when speaking. The sounds of speech are formed by relative movements of the larynx, lips, teeth and tongue, in conjunction with the flow of breath. The gestures are imbued with the same character as these subtler movements of the speech organs, and patients are encouraged to try to be aware of the inner expression which is associated with a given sound. For example, when making the vowel sound *ah,* the lips and teeth are open. The gesture associated with this sound is also open, and the sense of wonder or understanding, which it may convey in speech, is cultivated in the patient. By contrast, the mouth is more closed in the sound *oo,* and a quite different feeling is associated with it.

The sense of rhythm in speech, particularly as it is expressed in poetry, is also used therapeutically. Some rhythms express an extrovert quality, some a more inward contemplation, others more of a martial character. The proper balance of rhythms in the body is one of the hallmarks of health, and loss of rhythm is often part of the development of a disease. Therefore, the enlivenment of rhythm in the soul can have a very useful therapeutic effect. There are also exercises which can help a patient who is lacking a healthy sense of three-dimensional space. These are particularly useful when dealing with excessively introverted and sedentary people who may have withdrawn from full engagement with their

immediate environment. Experiences of the six directions of
three-dimensional space (up, down, left, right, forward and back)
may be accentuated by these exercises, which strengthen the activity of the ego and re-establish a confident connection with the
environment in people with agoraphobia and other irrational
fears.

Artistic therapists work together with doctors, nurses, therapeutic masseurs and hydrotherapists in anthroposophical practices and hospitals. Methods of working together have been
developed, such as case conferences (see Chapter 16), so that the
picture of the patient which is used as the basis for a powerful, integrated programme of treatment is as full as possible. The training undertaken by artistic therapists covers the various effects of
the many forms of their particular therapy. In practice, they have
to be creative themselves in evolving a series of exercises individually tailored to the needs of the patient. The exercise programme must be designed in such a way that it can respond to the
patient's progress, or to any difficulties that may arise during
treatment.

8. Therapeutic Massage and Hydrotherapy

All massage affects the skin and also the underlying muscles and soft tissue, which have a semi-fluid quality. The fluid parts of the body are where the etheric upbuilding processes express themselves most directly, but there is also an interplay of nervous stimulation in the muscles, and emotional disturbances can lead to subconscious muscular tension. In this sense, the muscular tension can be seen as an expression of the emotional and nervous condition of the patient. The tension, as is typical of the astral influence, consists of a loss of fluidity and a tendency towards rigidity. In an extreme form, it constitutes an illness.

The rhythmic system brings the head pole and metabolic pole into harmony. The rhythmic quality of natural cycles of activity — such as breathing in and out, and the systole and diastole of the heart's action — harmonize the opposing etheric and astral activities. With that in mind, Dr Ita Wegman and Dr Margarethe Hauschka developed a strongly rhythmical form of therapeutic massage. The rhythm in breathing tends to follow a pattern of in-breath and out-breath, with a pause before the next in-breath. In the massage, the kneading takes a progressively stronger hold of the tissue, then relaxes the hold, then there is a pause before the next stroke. There is an association between breathing in and waking up, and breathing out and relaxing. The kneading of the first part of the massage has a wakening quality, and the softer movement of the second, a quality more akin to going to sleep. This means there is first a predominance of astral activity (waking up), then of etheric activity (relaxing). Through the rhythmical alternation of the two in the tissues, a powerful local harmonizing effect can be achieved.

The natural movement of water is in curves, not straight lines.

The curves may be gentle or strong, and they may develop into spirals or vortices. The etheric body, or body of formative life forces, is strongly related to the watery, fluid element and has a natural kinship with curving forms. This expresses itself formatively in the curves and rounded shapes of the body, and it may be noted that people who have a constitutional predominance of metabolic (etheric) activity have more rounded bodies than those with predominant head (astral) activity, who tend to have more angular bodily features. The movements in the massage also take on this curved quality. Around the joints of the body, the curves may be quite tight, and form spiral movements. When massaging the back, they might follow a figure of eight and include the rhythmic alternation.

Sometimes the tips of the fingers are used during a massage, and the concentrated pressure this can produce makes the patient strongly aware of the affected area. This stimulates a breaking-down, dissolving effect in areas of hardening. On other occasions, when the palm of the hand is used, a much softer effect is achieved. As the pressure is released, the palm can be used to lift the tissues, with a kind of sucking effect. This creates a feeling of lightening and gives a strong sense of release.

The etheric forces have a unifying effect on the body. One of the hallmarks of living things, as opposed to purely mechanical systems, is that an activity or change in one area always exerts some influence on every other part of the organism. That the organs and tissues are not isolated in separate compartments has long been recognized and put to use in treatment by ancient eastern forms of medicine, such as acupuncture and reflexology. Acupuncturists use needles to stimulate a healing response in the body, but the needles tend to be inserted some way away from the site of the symptoms. In reflexology, the processes of the whole body are considered to be reflected in various parts of the feet. Reflexologists treat the feet to exert healing influences on problems elsewhere in the body. Conventional medicine cannot comprehend this, as it limits itself to treatment of the local pathological process.

Rhythmical massage often works on one part of the body in order to influence another. An excess of astral activity in one part of the body is likely to be accompanied by a deficit in another. For example, in tension headaches, it may be possible to relieve the headache by vigorously kneading the calves and feet. This is aimed at diverting the excess astral activity causing the spasm into the lower part of the body by stimulating astral activity in that area, and can bring a degree of relief immediately. Massage of the neck and the whole back, following a downward movement from the neck along the spine, may also help to relieve the neck and shoulder tension typical of these headaches.

During treatment, the masseur picks up many indications about the patient's bodily condition, which the physician would be unlikely to perceive in the same way. The distribution of muscular tension throughout the body becomes clear. A common finding is extreme tension and spasm in the neck and shoulders, perhaps extending down to the waist, with a relative lack of tension below the waist. The lack of tension can be just as extreme as the tension in the upper body and, in some cases, just as unhealthy. The masseur develops sensitivity to the condition and tone of the skin and soft tissues. In some patients, these may feel loose and unformed while, in others there is a sense of dried, hardened tautness. Considerable variations in the temperature of the skin are also noted.

A female patient might be referred to a therapeutic masseur with a band of extreme tension in the middle of her back, circling the trunk, muscular flaccidity and a marked coldness below it, and normal warmth in the upper body. The masseur might know from the doctor who referred the patient that she has suffered from a long-standing disorder of the reproductive organs since having had sexual and marital difficulties. When the doctor and masseur confer on their perceptions of the problem, an extended picture arises. It becomes clear that the knot of muscular tension around the trunk, the coldness and lack of tone below the waist, the chronic gynaecological problems, and the sexual and marital anxieties are all different expressions of the same problem. The conventional medical diagnosis could be that she has a chronic pelvic inflammatory disease, for example a longstanding, low-grade infection of the fallopian tubes. Adding to this diagnosis, the anthroposophical understanding of what lies behind the infection would be that the unconscious activity of the patient's ego is deficient in the pelvic region, as expressed in the lack of warmth.

Therapeutic help may be given on several levels, including massage, medicines and counselling. The massage might be aimed at bringing warmth and tone to the lower half of the body and releasing the knot of tension in the trunk. Breathing becomes more relaxed when this tension is relieved, and that releases a spontaneous flow of warmth into the lower body. Such an improvement may initially be temporary, and require a series of treatments to become self-sustaining. Once this point has been reached, improvements in the gynaecological symptoms are likely to follow. Medicines and counselling may be required to help achieve these changes.

Quite similar findings might arise for a patient suffering from illnesses of other organs in the lower abdomen, as in ulcerative colitis, which affects the large bowel. The masseur's observations assist the doctor in developing a detailed picture of the patient, and can directly indicate therapeutic possibilities by what they add to the overall picture.

The masseur is very conscious during treatment of the distribution of warmth in the body. In anthroposophical medicine, a disturbance in the warmth organization can be seen as a cause as well as a symptom, of illness. The warmth organization is the physical medium for the activity of the ego, and it has a potential for healing which can be exploited. To that end, warm, draught-free rooms are used for therapeutic massage, with only as much uncovering of the patient as is required for the treatment. Plant oils are used which lubricate the skin but also induce a warming effect on the body, and this effect can be enhanced by the inclusion of aromatic oils in a mixture. The masseur selects oils most suited to the patient and the type of healing response which is sought.

In conventional medicine, the use of preparations applied to the skin has been largely restricted to the use of ointments for local skin conditions. Only relatively recently have medicines been deliberately applied to the skin to be absorbed into the bloodstream as a way of treating internal conditions, such as angina. Anthroposophical medicine applies many substances externally for the purposes of influencing the body as a whole. For example,

ethereal plant oils may be used which are related to the mild catabolic, breaking-down processes the astral element introduces into
the flower. These oils, such as rosemary or lavender, can stimulate a response from the whole metabolic system if applied to the
skin during baths.

Of course, oil and water do not mix but, in treatment, an appa-
ratus is used which draws a thin stream of oil into a vortex of
water, creating a fine dispersion. The oil droplets are so fine that
they remain dispersed for a considerable time before separating
out. When patients are immersed in these oil-dispersion baths, the
whole skin is affected. They emerge with a very fine layer of oil
all over, which continues to have an effect if they are carefully
wrapped in a cotton sheet and blankets rather than dried off. After
spending about a quarter of an hour in the bath, and resting,
wrapped up, for another three-quarters of an hour, patients usually feel the warming effect of the oils for many more hours. The
bath itself is roughly body temperature, so it is the quality of the
oil, rather than the heat of the water, which brings about the profound warming. The effect of the treatment is that the ego is better able to exert its influence within the physical body and, as a
result, the patient feels inwardly quiet and composed. This form
of treatment is an anthroposophical development of hydrotherapy.

In addition to the warming quality of an oil-bath, each of the
ethereal oils has a specific effect. For example, lavender, with its
relaxing, soporific qualities, contrasts with rosemary, which has a
stronger toning, awakening effect. Rosemary also strongly stimulates the peripheral circulation, and for this reason can be used as
a local treatment in footbaths, when a warming effect in the feet
and legs is required.

Irregularities in the warmth organization can also be helped by
hydrotherapy. Cold areas in the lower body, especially in the pelvic
region as described above, often accompany gynaecological problems and these are particularly helped by baths containing melissa
(lemon balm) oil, which has a refreshing and gentle warming effect. Anxiety is often accompanied by areas of coldness (as in a
cold sweat), particularly in the legs and feet. This can be helped by
footbaths up to the knees containing rosemary. Warm footbaths
with mustard can be used in addition to vigorous massage of the

calves and feet in treating migraine attacks. The mustard reddens and mildly irritates the skin, diverting the excessive metabolic activity from the head into the calves and feet. In a similar way, warming footbaths can help to relieve an asthma attack.

A profound and long-standing problem with warmth is often found in patients with illnesses such as cancer and M.E. (myalgic encephalomyelitis, or post-viral fatigue syndrome). Such patients often have body temperatures nearer to 35 degrees Celsius than the normal 37 degrees. In healthy people, there is generally a rhythmical variation of their temperatures, most people being slightly warmer in the evening than they are first thing in the morning. Patients whose body temperatures are reduced tend to lack this regular rhythmical quality. Medical treatments for cancer and immune problems are dealt with in Chapter 13, but within the context of hydrotherapy special 'pyrogenic' baths can help by supporting a normalization of body temperature. The patient is immersed in water up to the chin for an hour, during which time the water is kept at, or just above, body temperature. The warming effect is not from the water but, in this case, from removing the body's ability to cool itself. The main method of cooling is the evaporation of sweat from the skin but, in the bath, the sweat goes into the bath instead of evaporating, and the cooling effect is lost.

A pyrogenic bath can raise the body temperature as high as 39 or 40 degrees Celsius and, if the patient has not had a feverish illness for years and has a subnormal temperature, is quite strenuous for the body. The patient's pulse and blood pressure must be carefully observed during the bath, and for an hour afterwards while resting in bed. It is not suitable for severely debilitated patients or those with serious heart problems, but its profound warming effect can make a valuable contribution to re-establishing a normal body temperature when this is lacking. To the anthroposophical doctor, it is important that the warmth is produced within the body rather than from outside. This is because the body's own warmth organization is an integral part of the whole person, just as much as the physical structure of the body. Warmth or cold forcibly introduced from outside is foreign to this organization in much the same way as a splinter is foreign to the physical structure.

Lying in baths, patients experience a degree of weightlessness through the buoyancy of the water, and this is helpful when there is difficulty in standing or walking, as in arthritis or following a stroke. However, hydrotherapy's primary effect is on bodily functions, such as the circulation, muscular tone and the distribution of warmth. Indirectly, it can also affect the soul, as there can be emotional reactions to the profound relaxing and warming effects. Similarly, in massage, the release of muscular tension can bring with it a release of pent-up or buried emotions.

The medium of hydrotherapy, water, is the medium in which we are suspended before birth. As the medium of the etheric forces, it has a special relationship with the healing processes of the body. The therapeutic potential of baths has been recognized since the time of Ancient Greece, when Hippocrates, who is known as the father of modern medicine, established a healing centre on the island of Cos, which included elaborate bathing facilities. Throughout Europe, recognition of the healing effects of bathing in water from certain springs led to the development of many spa towns, which still flourish in central Europe. Traditional medicine is less respected in Britain, where the therapeutic use of spas all but died out in the early 20th century. The conventional medical view, which rapidly dominated British culture, regarded the main use of hot spas, such as at Bath, to be as primitive sources of hot water, and their therapeutic value was lost to conventional practice.

Cultural factors have also played a part in bringing about a disregard for the importance of warmth in the maintenance of health. In winter, it is common to see men outdoors in shirtsleeves and women with little or no covering on their legs. Many offices and public buildings are kept very warm and, when people go in and out of such buildings, they often pay little attention to extreme temperature changes. Anthroposophical medicine sees the human warmth organization as the physical carrier of ego activity, with great importance for the maintenance of health. It is possible that the widespread inattention to keeping warm is a factor in the development of the many degenerative and sclerotic diseases, such as arteriosclerosis and osteoarthritis, which are the predominant contemporary health problems of the Western world. The range of hydrotherapy treatments can contribute to alleviating this damage. They can also give patients the opportunity to become more aware of their bodily warmth as a step towards becoming more responsible for their own health.

9. The Art of Nursing

Nurses have been deeply affected by the technical advances of conventional medicine. Their work has become increasingly specialized and, thereby, has been divided up. They have become responsible for technical tasks, such as measuring blood pressure and checking heart monitors, leaving many of the more personal aspects of their role to assistants and auxiliaries. There has also been an escalation of time-consuming paperwork in conventional medicine through the need to keep detailed records of the results of technical tests. While much good has come from the technical aspects of modern medicine, these developments have made it increasingly difficult for nurses to find enough time to establish personal contact with each patient and to give the care that good nursing demands.

Anthroposophy is able to integrate an understanding of the physical body and its ailments with an understanding of the spiritual element of the patient, and this has practical implications for nurses. For example, one of the differences between the nurse's role and the doctor's is that the nursing team cares for the patient 24 hours a day, seven days a week, whereas the doctor normally has contact with the patient only for short periods. Through this extended contact, the nurse has a special responsibility for supporting the rhythmical functions of the patient. The cycles of sleeping and waking, eating and bowel movements, activity and rest, when properly regulated, support the healing process. Neglect can have the opposite effect because, in times of illness, patients may not be able to maintain healthy rhythms themselves.

Nurses who wish to practise anthroposophical medicine must complete a conventional nursing qualification before supplementing it with anthroposophical training. In many ways, the anthroposophical approach is in accordance with the best of conventional nursing philosophy, but it tends to lay greater emphasis on particular areas.

The nurse's task is defined as assisting people in those activities which contribute to health, or to its recovery, or to a peaceful death, which the patients would do for themselves if they had the necessary strength, will or knowledge. Nursing also helps patients to follow prescribed therapy and to become independent of assistance as quickly as possible.

In practice, nursing generally involves caring for the physical environment of the patient. This may include ensuring that the bed gives adequate support, the surroundings are clean and warm, and there is plenty of fresh air. An anthroposophical nurse will also be aware of what might be described as the patient's soul environment. This includes everything taken in by the senses — the quality of light in the room, the colours, sounds and smells, and also the aesthetic quality of the surroundings, as it is beneficial for the patient to have things of beauty to focus on. It also includes the avoidance, if possible, of anything lacking in aesthetic quality, which can have a far stronger effect on someone lying ill in bed than it would on a healthy person.

The soul environment also includes the mood the nurse brings to the patient and, for this reason, it is important what frame of mind the nurse is in when entering the sick room. It may be necessary to pause in order to adopt the calmness and openness necessary to allow an appropriate response to the patient's needs. A state of hurry or irritation or, for that matter, an exaggerated geniality, would get in the way of being receptive to the patient. On the level of the soul, patients need emotional warmth and support from their nurses just as much as, on the physical level, they need a warm room to assist recovery.

The nurse also needs to help the patient in a social sense. At a given time, there may be a need for peace, privacy and rest but, depending on the patient and the stage of the illness, at another time it may be important to mix with other patients and to be involved in social and cultural activities. Attending stimulating talks or musical evenings, for example, or going for walks in the countryside can rekindle an interest in life, which may be therapeutic in itself.

The patient's warmth organization can be greatly supported by the application of ethereal plant oils by the nurse. In their training, anthroposophical nurses learn a technique of application of these oils which is similar to therapeutic massage.[1] It tends to concentrate on the soothing, balancing movements which encourage the flow of the etheric, upbuilding processes, rather than the more vigorous kneading actions associated with stimulating consciousness in a particular area. Use of the oils can stimulate warmth in areas where it may well be deficient, such as the neck, shoulders, back, abdomen, feet and lower legs. It can also produce a feeling of well-being and provide great comfort to patients who are dying and feeling lonely or frightened about what they are facing, particularly at the stage when words are inadequate. Such treatment often helps to provide a feeling of security in which deep-seated fears can be released and discussed in a way that would not come about in normal conversation.

Oils, or ointments, are chosen according to the particular needs and condition of each patient. During their application, the nurse gains a sense of the patient's skin and muscle tone areas of relative warmth and cold in the body, and also indications of the patient's emotional state. As with the similar observations of the therapeutic masseur, these indications are very helpful to the doctor, particularly as many of the nursing treatments are given on a daily basis.

Such treatments are usually prescribed by the doctor, but nurses might also apply oils on their own initiative. For example, if a patient has difficulty getting to sleep at night, a nurse might apply a back massage of lavender oil, as this has a very relaxing effect. The personal contact between nurse and patient is also important because it adds an invaluable emotional warmth to the treatment. Not only can the use of lavender oil obviate the need for a sleeping tablet, but it is also an entirely different experience for both patient and nurse. The application of oils has a special role in supporting the treatment of patients with symptoms of anxiety and other emotional problems, and also patients who are physically very weak and may be bed-bound.

The nurse further complements the work of the therapeutic masseur and the hydrotherapist in the administration of baths and footbaths. Stimulating footbaths containing rosemary in the morning and relaxing ones with lavender in the evening form a regular part of nursing treatment. Mustard footbaths may be administered by nurses to alleviate certain kinds of headaches, asthmatic attacks and bronchitis, and at the first signs of a panic attack. They may also be used at the first signs of the onset of a headache or a cold. As it is so important to apply the treatment early in the development of the symptoms, nurses are often called upon to act promptly on their own initiative in such cases.

Nurses must have a good knowledge of the characteristics of the substances they use in treatment, particularly herbs. Each one needs to be used in a specific way to release the healing properties to the maximum effect. For example, flowers need delicate handling if their therapeutic properties are to be enhanced rather than destroyed by insensitive preparation, such as infusing them for too long. Infusions made from roots, stems, seeds and leaves each require a particular simmering time. Mechanical or unthinking preparation reduces, and can even nullify, the therapeutic effect, and the nurse must be familiar with each remedy to get the best from it.

A plant with many therapeutic uses is camomile, which is particularly effective as a soothing agent. An infusion of the flowers can be given as an inhalation to help relieve and clear sinusitis or bronchitis, or as a gargle and mouthwash for mouth infections. In a hip bath it is good for soothing the genital region after childbirth. Camomile may also be used in a compress prepared from an infusion of the flowers. It is applied to the patient's skin as hot as possible without being painful, and covered with another cloth before a third, woollen layer is wrapped around the body and secured with safety pins. This keeps the compress in position and helps to retain the heat. A hot-water bottle placed on top of the woollen layer adds to the warmth, and the patient is tucked up in bed to rest for at least half an hour. Used on the abdomen, such a compress can be very helpful in a variety of metabolic and digestive disturbances. Camomile is strongly indicated when there are spasms or cramps, especially as in indigestion or period pains.

By contrast, a lemon compress is prepared in lukewarm water. Applied to the feet and calves, it can help limit the extent of a high fever when there is a risk of the patient becoming delirious or, in children, when there is a risk of febrile convulsions. Such treatment can help to avoid the automatic use of paracetamol and similar drugs, whose dangers for health in the long-term are described in Chapter 10.

Compresses, oils and ointments are also regularly applied by nurses to have an effect on the major organs. A warm cloth with an ointment containing lavender and rose oil placed over the heart helps to calm palpitations in cases of anxiety or in the heart conditions of the elderly. Copper ointment applied over the kidneys also has a local warming effect and helps to restore harmony to their activity. Compresses are often applied over the liver for patients with problems in that area, and also in some cases of depression, when it is beneficial to stimulate the vitality of the metabolic organs.

Anthroposophical nurses are trained in the techniques of preparing and administering all these treatments, many of which would appear quite foreign to nurses who are only conventionally trained. Through extending their skills with such practical techniques, nurses often find they get much more fulfilment from their work. As well as more personal contact with patients, anthroposophical nursing involves much more direct contact with the materials, such as plants, from which remedies are made.

In anthroposophical hospitals and clinics, the nurses administer the medicines prescribed by doctors, just as they would in conventional practice. Above and beyond the concentration and accuracy required for this, anthroposophical nurses cultivate a reverence and deep feeling for the qualities of the medicinal substances. They do not need the detailed knowledge the doctor must have to prescribe the medicines, but it is important that they understand some of the fundamental principles if they are to administer the medicines effectively. Whether the treatment involves giving a medicine, applying an oil, or any other techniques the nurse concentrates outwardly on performing the task correctly, and inwardly on the qualities of the substances being used and the nature of the treatment.

Nurses work together as a team providing twenty-four hour care, and the provision of consistency and continuity in treatment is dependent on their ability to communicate accurately and effectively with one another. Their role as communicators, combined with

their observations of patients over long periods, also enables them
to assist in the doctor's meetings with patients. Often, patients need
to hear what the doctor has to say several times before grasping it
fully, and nurses may be able to explain it more personally through
the closer relationships they have built up with them. Similarly, patients sometimes find it easier to discuss with nurses certain matters
which the doctor ought to know and, in these cases, the nurse can
tactfully pass on the information. The vital communicative role also
applies in sharing knowledge with other therapists, such as a therapeutic masseur or artistic therapist who, like the doctor, might see
the patient for shorter periods. The nurse keeps them informed of
the patient's mental and physical state, and ensures that periods of
therapy do not adversely affect important aspects of the patient's
daily rhythm. The closer contact nurses have with patients also
means that they are often able to help in difficult communications
with friends and relatives.

Anthroposophical nurses fulfil a central role by bringing all the
individual aspects of treatment together and ensuring that they
form a harmonious whole rather than, through poor communication, working against each other. The anthroposophical approach
aims to humanize every aspect of the nurse's work, restoring the
personal contact that has been lost in the technical specialization
of conventional nursing. Each and every activity is accompanied
by an awareness of, and reverence for, the task of caring for a patient who is not just another physical body in a bed, but someone
who has a soul and a spirit.

10. Childhood Illnesses

From conception and on into childhood, the human spirit is involved in shaping the physical body which is to be its vehicle for a life on earth. This activity is particularly intense between conception and birth, and in the first few years of life — the time of maximum growth and maturation. While this is happening, eating and sleeping dominate the infant's daily life. Through the newly formed physical body, the child is influenced by heredity and environmental factors. At birth, these influences are very strong and the body is, to some extent, foreign to the spirit incarnating into it. The spirit must increasingly make the body its own, especially in the first seven years, when it remoulds it in a way that might be compared to the breaking in of new shoes.

This first seven-year phase of childhood is concluded by the change of teeth, which is a dramatic expression of the extent of the remoulding process. The enamel of the teeth is the hardest substance in the human body, and in later life cannot be renewed. Only this once does the renewal of the constituents of the body include the teeth. The second phase of childhood leads to puberty, at around twelve to fourteen. The third leads to adulthood, at about eighteen to twenty-two, when the process of physical maturity is complete These phases of bodily development are accompanied by changes in the development of the person as a whole.

Following the change of teeth, the formative life forces (etheric forces), which were previously so involved in reshaping the body, become partially freed from this role, particularly in the case of the system of nerves and senses. They then become available as forces of mental creativity and can be applied to, for example, the formal learning of reading, writing and arithmetic. This allows more serious teaching to begin, replacing the learning by imitation of the earlier phase. The emancipation of the etheric body represents a step in the process of the child's independence from its parents. The predominance of the physical body in the first phase, when it is being remoulded, is replaced by a predominance of the etheric processes during the second phase As they are also the processes of healing and revitalization, this phase tends to be a time of particularly good health.

At puberty, there is an awakening of sexual drives and turbulent emotions. From the anthroposophical point of view, this is the time of the awakening, or freeing, of the astral body, which had previously been bound up with the processes of growth and development. During this third phase, there is a powerful demand for personal independence, but without the developed sense of responsibility, which tends to come later (about eighteen to twenty-one) with the awakening of the ego. This is generally recognized in so far as adult rights and responsibilities are given at this time, rather than at the time of reproductive maturity in the early teens.

As can be seen from the above, only the physical body becomes completely independent at birth and there is a kind of birth of the etheric body around seven, of the astral body around fourteen and the ego at about twenty-one. These ages are by no means fixed and individual paths of development can vary widely. Also, this does not mean that a young child does not already have its own etheric body, astral body or ego, but that they are partially freed from their unconscious activity in the processes of growth and maturation at around these ages and become more available to the personality. Before puberty, for example, the astral forces are particularly involved in maturing the reproductive organs. Afterwards, they arouse powerful emotions and desires and produce a determination to make decisions for oneself.

Against this background, the role of illness during childhood, particularly in the first seven years, can be seen in a quite different light from the conventional view. The opportunity for remoulding the physical body is provided by the constant dissolving and re-forming of its structures. During feverish illnesses, all the metabolic processes speed up and the high temperatures can offer a special opportunity for a more intensive reshaping. Fevers are often accompanied by a loss of weight, reflecting the preponderance of breaking-down processes that take place Many observant parents and teachers notice that children look a little more mature after such an illness. They may also seem more composed and less prone to irritability than before the illness.

Small children often have very many feverish infections, especially soon after starting at a playgroup or school. This is generally recognized to be the result of meeting many of the bacteria and viruses carried by humans for the first time, and needing to build up immunity to them. For some time after birth, particularly if the baby is breast-fed, the child is protected by the mother's immunity, but the time comes when the child must develop its own immunity. In measles especially, there is a profound activation of the immune system, with many antibodies produced. In the past, when children got measles it was common for doctors to regard it as the coming to maturity of the immune system. They would tell parents of children who were having many minor illnesses that they would be much more resistant once they had recovered from measles. Nowadays, virtually all conventional doctors try to prevent the major childhood infections, such as measles, mumps and whooping cough, through an extensive vaccination programme

Doctors still recognize that the many coughs and colds that appear when the child starts school are part of this developing maturity and not a sign of serious ill-health, but this does not prevent them from prescribing medicines like paracetamol to suppress the fever, and antibiotics to kill the bacteria on the body's behalf. This is in spite of the fact that, in seventy-five to eighty per cent of cases, the body would have been capable of overcoming the infection itself. Only the minority requires medical treatment.

It is becoming apparent that this use of medicines discourages the body's own healing processes and even, in the case of the suppression of fever, weakens them. Antibiotics have been widely used to treat infections since the 1940s and 1950s. Since then, the medical profession has become increasingly aware of a wide variety of diseases caused by abnormal immune responses, but few conventional doctors have questioned whether these two facts might be connected. The abnormal responses can take the form of auto-immunity, when the immune system attacks the tissues of the body itself, or there may be an excessive response to foreign substances in the form of an allergy.

For example, hayfever is an excessive reaction by the immune system to pollen in the eyes and nasal membranes. Asthma is also thought to be caused by this kind of mechanism. Not only is asthma becoming more common, but more children and adults are dying from it despite ever-stronger drugs becoming available to control it. The appearance of what seems to be a completely new illness in which the immune system breaks down — acquired immune deficiency syndrome, or Aids — might also be taken to suggest that the increasing number of people suffering from such disorders may be connected with the widespread and indiscriminate use of antibiotics and paracetamol, which weaken the immune system.

At the centre of the immune system is the body's ability to distinguish between foreign substances and the bodily tissues. This can only be achieved by having a highly developed sense of identity which extends right down to the molecular level, as the immune system must be able to distinguish the bodily tissues from inorganic material, from substances originating in plants and animals, and also from substances originating in other humans. This ability is therefore specific to the individual concerned. During childhood, the immune system is maturing at the same time as the ego is working to make the physical body its own, putting its own stamp of identity on the mixture of inherited characteristics. The inflammatory childhood infections offer special opportunities for the individual identity to be stamped more deeply into the substance of the body. The warmth of the fever is analogous to the warmth that melts sealing wax and allows the impression of a signet ring to be stamped into it as a sign of the owner's identity.

It follows from this that a suppression of the natural course of an infection will have detrimental consequences as well as short-term benefits. The same will be the case with the artificial prevention of diseases like measles, mumps and whooping cough, which used to be thought of as the normal illnesses of childhood. If the ego is prevented from making the body its own during early childhood, a foreign element remains for the rest of the life. Foreign substances and processes within the body are characteristic of the sclerotic (hardening) and degenerative diseases of later life, and an increase in these is to be expected as a result of such interference with the development of the immune system. The link would appear to be supported by a study published in *The Lancet* which found that children who have measles with a rash (i.e. the illness develops fully) have a lower incidence of cancer and degenerative joint disease in later life than those who do not develop a rash.[1] It is perhaps no coincidence that the sclerotic and degenerative diseases, such as cancer, heart attacks and strokes, are the main causes of death in the Western world, where vaccination against measles routinely takes place.

Anthroposophical medicine offers a range of remedies aimed at stimulating and supporting the body's own healing response to infection. For example, homeopathically prepared belladonna (deadly nightshade) or argentum (silver) can be used to moderate excessive fever without completely suppressing it. This may be particularly important in cases where there is a risk of febrile convulsions or if the fever makes the child delirious. Lemon compresses applied to the calves and feet can also be used to control a fever. In the majority of infections, the child recovers without the use of antibiotics or fever-suppressing drugs. When the infection is more serious, antibiotics may be required. For example, in severe illnesses such as bacterial meningitis, antibiotics are essential to save the child's life.

Space does not allow for a detailed account of the various childhood illnesses, many of which require medical attention. However, there follow some examples of how home remedies can be used to treat common complaints.[2]

Teething tends to be a cause of considerable discomfort for the child. It can usually be relieved by giving the baby something hard to bite on, and Camomile D3 pills dissolved in a teaspoon of water every couple of hours. Alternatively, the gums can be massaged with Weleda mouthwash.

Colds can be treated with Ferrum Phos. comp. pills which, again, may be dissolved in a teaspoon of water for babies.[3]

Middle-ear infections are often very painful, and should always be referred to a doctor, but they do not usually require antibiotics. They can be relieved by applying a warm onion compress to the ear and giving medicine such as Apis/Levisticum, as prescribed. To make a compress, finely chop a medium-sized onion, tie or fold it inside a cloth, warm it on a hot-water bottle and secure it against the ear with a woollen scarf or balaclava. If the child is old enough to co-operate, it helps to have the affected side of the head laid against a hot-water bottle to keep the compress and the ear warm.

Sore throats can be treated by gargling with sage tea or Weleda mouthwash, by sucking sage pastilles, or by taking Cinnabar/Pyrites tablets. Again, in most cases, antibiotics are not necessary.

Younger children are obviously very dependent on other people to look after them, particularly their mothers. Only by example do they learn to stand, walk and talk. Their dependency on, and sensitivity to, their environments mean they are very easily influenced by the moods and attitudes of others, especially their parents. They are also strongly influenced by sense impressions from the world around them. Because of this, anthroposophical doctors emphasize the importance of natural and aesthetic environments for young children. It is also important that they exercise their imaginations by playing with simple toys made from natural materials. These require the child's active participation to make them represent cars or babies, rather than synthetic toys, which are more exact copies of the real thing and therefore demand less of the imagination.

Consciousness has a destructive effect on the body, but this is greatly reduced during sleep. Daydreaming, creative play and fantasy fall between the fully awake state and the sleeping state of dreaming, and also have a less catabolic effect on the body. Especially in the first seven years of childhood, healthy development requires that the upbuilding, anabolic forces predominate. Only after the ages of six or seven should the etheric forces — which are involved in growth, including the development of the nervous system — begin to be called upon for intellectual work as part of a more formal education. Until then, children should be involved in creative play, practical activities such as baking, and artistic activities such as painting, singing and eurythmy. It is also beneficial for them to be told imaginative stories. This is the approach adopted by Rudolf Steiner schools (also known as Waldorf schools). If children are encouraged to learn reading, writing and arithmetic before they are ready, their etheric forces are called upon to fulfil an intellectual role before they have completed their formative work on the physical body. This weakens the physical constitution, which may result in tiredness, poor concentration, headaches, a proneness to recurrent infections, and a tendency to degenerative diseases in later life. The untimely intellectual development brings on a premature ageing process which can have harmful effects throughout life.

When reading, writing, arithmetic and foreign languages begin to be learnt, they should be taught in as imaginative and artistic a fashion as possible to children from six or seven up to about fourteen. This helps to prevent an overburdening of the body with the catabolic effects of abstract thought by balancing it with imaginative and creative activity. It also helps to produce a more balanced person in later life who is still able to be creative, and has a developed aesthetic sense as well as a capacity for clear thought. This approach to education, which began in the 1920s, is followed by Rudolf Steiner schools throughout the world. Although there has been a recognition in state education of the importance of balancing factual learning with the active participation of children finding things out for themselves, there remains a shortsighted conviction that the earlier children learn to read and write, the better.

Anthroposophical doctors regard an education which works in harmony with the natural development of the child as one of the most important elements of preventive medicine. The contribution an appropriate education can make to health, in both childhood and adulthood, is enormous. It was described earlier how an imbalance in the soul can cause illness. A teacher in a Rudolf Steiner school aims to spot such tendencies as they begin to appear and to find a way to harmonize them. An excessively slow and dreamy child would need a quite different educational approach from a prematurely intellectual and hyperactive one. Whenever possible, anthroposophical doctors work alongside the teachers, supporting the preventive medical aspect of their work.[4]

The main contribution of anthroposophical medicine to the treatment of childhood illnesses comes from the understanding gained by regarding childhood as a time when the ego is remoulding the

physical body. Parents, doctors and teachers can help this process
so that the child's body becomes a vehicle which is able to serve the
ego healthily throughout life. The way the child's own healing
forces are supported by the doctor during illness is seen to have
consequences for the rest of the life. However, love and wise care
from parents and teachers can have an even more profound effect
on the child's health than medical treatment. The doctor, therefore,
also has a special role as advisor to the parents and teachers on the
medical aspects of the child's development.

11. Inner Development

The growth and development that takes place during childhood is obvious, particularly because the physical changes are so dramatic. Although not so outwardly obvious, the rest of life continues this process of development. From the age of thirty, a noticeable physical decline can be observed, but there need not be a similar decline in the development of the soul and spirit. Our inner development, which is observable to an extent in personality, is increasingly in our own hands as we mature. Through anthroposophy, we can become more aware of how to take responsibility for it.

Many opportunities for development arise in life, which often come in the form of crises or problems. These challenges may be unique to the person concerned or, because life is also strongly coloured by natural biological changes that affect us all, they may be common to everyone. There are certain spiritual and psychological stages of development that are typical of particular phases in life, and an understanding of these can help enormously in coming to terms with the problems as they arise

The first phase of adult life runs through the twenties, from about twenty-one to twenty-eight, and tends to be very strongly influenced by the powerful feelings and emotions which began to stir during puberty. It is a time of searching for an identity and direction in life, and perhaps also for a life partner. There is usually a great amount of energy — all-night parties are perfectly manageable, and the prospect of hitch-hiking around the world holds no fears. This phase is also generally the time when the career begins and the first home is established. The process of finding the right work, and the right partner, is at the same time a process of finding oneself and a set of values and aims to live by.

In the next phase, from about twenty-eight to thirty-five, a more serious note generally appears, with the direction in life becoming clearer. Priorities which may have been worked out during the twenties now become more important. The vitality of youth begins to be limited, and illnesses often occur at this time if a continuation of the lifestyle of the twenties is attempted. Exhaustion, anxiety or mild depression may force a recognition of the priorities in life and the realization that they should be upheld more earnestly. Life is no longer a game. There is also a need to organize, to achieve advancement at work perhaps, or to keep on top of running a home. Different needs have to be balanced in an increasingly busy life, especially if, as is often the case, there are small children to look after. The twenty-one to twenty-eight period is characterized by the sensitivity of the emotional aspect of the soul, and is called in anthroposophy the phase of the *sentient soul*. The twenty-eight to thirty-five period is associated with the practical application of the intellect, and is called the phase of the *intellectual soul*.

By the time of the next phase, around thirty-five to forty-two, people have often mastered many of the demands of their work, and may even have attained their career goals. However, this is a time when nagging doubts often arise. There tends to be a questioning of whether it would be fulfilling to continue in the same career for the next twenty or twenty-five years, and long-standing relationships might seem stale. Deeper questions about the meaning of life may also arise, representing a more spiritual appraisal of the life to date These questions are concerned with a greater objectivity and awareness of the implications of one's actions, and are related to a third aspect of the soul, the will. The thirty-five to forty-two phase is called the period of the *consciousness soul*.

The physical decline becomes more apparent from forty-two to forty-nine, most dramatically for women in the menopause. The challenge of this phase is to identify with wider needs and interests; for example, looking beyond what has already been achieved in the career, or finding a new role as young children mature and leave home. The more there is an identification with the needs and concerns of others, the more spiritual advancement takes place. This personal development can, to an extent, bring an inner freedom from the physical body's decline

In the next phase, from forty-nine to fifty-six, much depends on whether this development has taken place, because clinging to past achievements inevitably brings painful experiences. For example, at work, people in this phase often feel increasingly threatened by rising younger colleagues. It is much better all round for the older person to act as mentor and benefactor to the younger ones rather than to try to hold them back for fear of competition.

Between fifty-six and sixty-three, the experiences of the previous phase are intensified as the prospect of retirement looms. Thoughts of death bring on a questioning of values and priorities, and of what has been achieved in the life. The progress made in earlier periods towards a true wisdom and understanding increasingly influences how older people are able to handle what life brings them. After sixty-three, and particularly after seventy, what is achieved has more significance for humanity as a whole than for the individual's personal development. The differences between the lives led by old people can be very striking, with some able to be highly creative and inwardly active despite the physical body's degeneration, while others succumb inwardly to the physical decline. Once again, this has much to do with the development achieved in earlier phases.

From birth to death, we are all undergoing a process of inner development, even though we are generally unaware of its full significance. The situations we face on a daily basis make demands of us that act as a kind of schooling. However, throughout history, there have been methods of training which have focused on particular aspects of inner development, in some cases leading to direct perception of the spiritual realm. In Ancient Egypt, for example, there were schools teaching this knowledge. A master guided a chosen pupil through an arduous series of inner exercises aimed at purification of the soul. The training usually required withdrawal from everyday life into a temple, and took place in great secrecy. The insights gained through spiritual perceptions were generally used to benefit the culture as a whole, rather than the individual. For example, methods of cultivation were discovered and improved in this way.

Various forms of training for inner development have been practised down the centuries, particularly by religious orders. In the Middle Ages, Christians established monasteries and convents where they upheld strict vows and practised rigorous meditative exercises. But a significant change had taken place between the time of the Ancient Egyptian temple schools and the later Christian practices. It is not only the human physical form that has been affected by evolution: consciousness itself has also changed. Before the time of Christ, the human ego was not sufficiently developed for people to be able to bring about their own inner development. Hence, the Ancient Egyptian training required the complete submission of the pupil, who was prepared by others in such a way that spiritual perception was eventually attained.

Since the time of Christ, the ego has become capable of bringing about self-development, such that spiritual perception may be achieved through people's own efforts. A new process of inner training became necessary which would be appropriate for the changes that had taken place in the ego. This new path is inherent in Christ's life and teachings but, as humanity evolves, His works have to be interpreted into forms which the human consciousness of the time finds accessible. A form of training appropriate for the current era is contained within anthroposophy. Details are beyond the scope of this book but interested readers will find a thorough account in Steiner's *Knowledge of the Higher Worlds* (Rudolf Steiner Press). Guidance on inner training is also provided by the School of Spiritual Science, within the Anthroposophical Society.

In ancient times, the training was conducted by a chosen few in great secrecy, and the pupil played a passive role. Nowadays, it is essential that the motivation to undertake inner training comes from the pupils themselves, who make their own decisions and take responsibility for their own self-development. They should retain their freedom at all times and on no account submit to the will of a guru. The anthroposophical training is open to anyone and does not require a withdrawal from everyday life — on the contrary, it is to be hoped that it would lead to a deeper involvement.

Those who undertake such a training should be under no illusions about direct spiritual perception, which is fully attained only at a very advanced stage. The first level of spiritual perception is consciousness in the etheric world, the realm of formative forces. Further development leads to direct perception of the astral, or soul, world. The third stage is consciousness in the world of the ego itself. The barrier between consciousness of the physical and spiritual worlds may be seen as a threshold. It is crossed on birth and death, when our awareness enters and leaves the physical world.

Everyone has latent organs for spiritual perception, and their development requires the inner strengthening necessary to make it possible to cross this threshold during life without losing consciousness. Knowledge of this threshold, how it can be crossed, and the results of crossing it unprepared, is essential to the anthroposophical doctor. It provides an understanding of many psychiatric symptoms, and other behavioural problems which are becoming increasingly apparent in contemporary culture, such as anxiety, addiction and anti-social behaviour.

12. Psychiatry

Anthroposophical doctors look beyond physical symptoms at how the ego and astral body are involved in causing illness, and take these considerations into account in treatment. In mental illness, the reverse is true — causes of mental and emotional symptoms are looked for in the physical and etheric bodies. In his first course of lectures to doctors, Rudolf Steiner proposed this challenging philosophy, suggesting that psychotherapy may be most valuable when used to treat physical illnesses and that mental illnesses generally required medical treatment.

It has been seen how it is possible to develop higher forms of consciousness which enable direct perception of the spiritual realm. The first stage is perception of the etheric world — the world of formative life forces. These powerful spiritual forces drive the building and renewal of the physical body, a constant process involving the transformation of matter. In our normal, physical consciousness, we have no direct perception of these etheric processes but, when they are perceived with etheric consciousness, the impressions are more powerful and have a greater sense of reality than physical perceptions. This is sometimes found to be a feature of the experiences of patients suffering from mental illness. Some schizophrenics, in particular, find their hallucinations and delusions to be more powerful than their physical sense impressions.

Anthroposophical doctors see a connection between such experiences and spiritual perception, but consider the schizophrenic's experiences to be pathological. Someone who has developed direct perception of the spiritual realm has the inner strength to shut out such perceptions at will and concentrate exclusively on the physical world. In schizophrenia, the patient tends to be overpowered by the experiences and is often unable to relate normally to the physical world — consciousness of the two worlds, or the two sides of the threshold, is usually confused.

In conventional psychiatry, mental illnesses include psychoses and neuroses, with psychoses tending to be the more serious. Schizophrenia and manic depression are examples of psychoses, which often involve delusions and disordered thinking, although the patient may be unaware of being ill. Neuroses, on the other hand, include anxiety, certain forms of depression, and obsessional, compulsive and phobic problems. These are deeply disturbing and unpleasant experiences for the patient, but generally leave thinking and understanding more or less intact. The patient is aware of the problem and, therefore, may be more concerned about it than someone with a psychosis.

The two main symptoms of schizophrenia are characteristic delusions and hearing voices. A typical delusion of schizophrenics is that their thoughts and feelings directly affect the outside world. For examples a patient might be feeling angry, then hear on the news that people have died in a rail crash and become convinced that the feelings of anger caused the crash. Alternatively, schizophrenics may feel that their thoughts are brought about by processes outside them. For example, they might believe that machinery in a nearby building causes them to think certain thoughts, or that other people are putting ideas into their heads. Another example of a typical delusion is the belief that something they may have read, say in a newspaper, refers to them, even though it is clear to everyone else that there is no connection. This symptom is closely related to what are known as paranoid delusions, when patients are convinced that others are talking secretly about them, usually negatively, and possibly plotting to do something evil against them.

An auditory hallucination usually takes the form of hearing someone who is not there talking about the patient. Typically, the voice says unpleasant things about the patient, and may even encourage self-inflicted injury. Psychiatrists usually interpret the hearing of voices as an indication that patients are experiencing their own thoughts as if they belonged to others. Normally, we feel completely independent from the outside world, with our own independent thoughts. A boundary is experienced between us and the rest of the world, which leaves our thinking free from external causes and the world free from our direct mental influence. From the symptoms described, it is clear that this boundary breaks down in schizophrenia.

When thoughts are experienced as if they belonged to others, it is as though the boundary between the inner and the outer had shifted, leaving the thoughts on the outside. The thinking processes then appear to be taken over by the laws of cause and effect of the outer, physical world and the normal sense of identity is lost. As was described in Chapter 4, self-consciousness, free will, reflective thinking and a sense of identity are characteristics of the human spirit. Although the spirit itself is eternal and cannot become ill, the loss of identity and free-thinking which takes place in schizophrenia indicates how the illness reaches right to the patient's inner core, distorting the spirit's union with the astral, etheric and physical bodies.

The etheric forces, which build and constantly maintain the physical body, obviously work into the physical realm. As was seen earlier, the sense organs and nervous system do not need the full activity of these life forces once they are fully formed, and what is then released is used in the activity of thinking. However, in the other systems of the body, particularly the metabolic region, the life forces need to be continually active in the transformation of substances in the organs. They should be engaged in this activity within the metabolic and rhythmic organs until death. Hallucinations and other symptoms of major mental illnesses occur when this breaks down — when life forces, which should be fully engaged in the activity of one of the organs of the metabolic or rhythmic systems, become free and invade the activity of thinking.

Unlike the forces released from the organs of the nerve-sense system, which provide for free thinking, the life forces from the metabolic and rhythmic systems have such power that they overwhelm the mental processes. The hallucinations they create can seem more real than the sense impressions of the physical world, such that the normal, healthy separation of the inner self from outer physical events is lost. So the relationships between the etheric and physical bodies in the organs of the metabolic and rhythmic systems should be looked at when such mental symptoms appear. Usually, changes in the etheric activity of the organ are responsible for the illness, rather than actual physical changes, although the physical changes associated with high fever can give rise to similar changes in consciousness. The toxic effects of some hallucinogenic drugs can also do so, and use of these drugs can induce schizophrenia.

The symptoms of schizophrenia are usually unpleasant and very disturbing although, occasionally, patients become attached to them, as might a user of hallucinogenic drugs. They are over-powered by the hallucinations to such an extent that they lose their freedom and identity and, in extreme situations, can no longer be held totally responsible for their actions. When they are unable to look after themselves, the psychiatrist has to be respon-sible for them until they are well enough to return to a more nor-mal life. This is the basis for assessing the need for compulsory admissions and treatment, if patients appear to be putting them-selves or others in danger.

Acute schizophrenia illustrates the need for an emphasis on medical rather than psychological forms of treatment, at least in the first instance. During an acute attack, the value of counselling or psychotherapy is usually very limited, doing little more than helping the patient to feel to some extent understood and sup-ported. Attempts to analyse the delusions, or to show that they are not real, are usually futile and only cause further upset. In this sit-uation, anthroposophical practice is able to offer a variety of med-icines, which help to reconnect the life forces with the organs in which they should be fully active. For example, stibium (antimo-ny) has this effect and may be given by injection in a homeopath-ic potency selected by the doctor. It is often necessary to use conventional psychiatric drugs as well, at least for a limited peri-od. The initial treatment may be followed by the use of artistic therapies, eurythmy therapy and sculpture therapy, which help to calm the patient and further assist in reuniting the life forces with their proper organs.

During an acute attack, a patient may have dramatic experi-ences, and may well be in a highly excitable state. However, those who have suffered from severe forms of schizophrenia for some years are often left in a 'flattened' emotional state, with very little motivation. It is as if the life forces which produced the dramatic symptoms had been burnt up and were no longer available, leaving the sufferer depleted of emotional and mental vitality. Such patients used to be referred to as 'burnt-out schizophrenics.' Although the initial therapeutic emphasis is medical, artistic therapies can make a useful contribution to treating this stage by bringing colour back to the patient's inner life, which has become dulled and grey. Also, after acute attacks, it is often valuable to discuss with patients what they have been through, thereby helping them to gain some insight into the nature of the illness and what they can do to make further attacks less likely.

Just as the physical body consists of various organs, the etheric body is differentiated into various parts, and these are intimately connected with the physical organs. The different characteristics of the mental illnesses can be used to identify the organ associated with the illness, because the characteristics point to the etheric forces connected with that organ. Steiner identified the heart and lung from the rhythmic

system, and the liver and kidney from the metabolic system, as the four organs principally involved in mental illness.

The ego, astral body and etheric body are active in every organ of the body, but their relative activity varies from organ to organ. It has already been described how the ego is particularly expressed through warmth (element of fire), the astral body through gases (air), the etheric body through fluids (water), and the physical body through

solids (earth). So, if an organ has characteristics that relate it particularly to, say, the watery element, this points to a predominance of etheric activity in that organ.

The liver, for example, has a striking fluidity, indicating just such a centre of etheric activity. It is itself semi-fluid, its shape being governed by the surrounding structure, and through it there passes a constant stream of different fluids. There are arteries and veins carrying blood, and channels for lymph and bile It is also one of only two organs in the body having a vein (carrying blood which is rich in carbon dioxide and low in oxygen) entering as well as leaving it. Such concentrations of carbon dioxide and low levels of oxygen are associated with vegetative growth. Plants use carbon dioxide to create sugars, which they store as starches, and it is the liver that is the body's prime store of sugar — in the form of glycogen, also known as animal starch. Like plants, the liver is dominated by upbuilding, anabolic activity in its vast catalogue of biochemical processes. Even in its role as neutralizer of poisons, it generally renders them harmless by adding a substance (usually a sugar) to them so that they can be safely excreted, rather than breaking them down in what would be a catabolic process.

The production of bile and its collection in the gall bladder is a quite distinct exception to the liver's mainly anabolic processes. Bile is created by the breaking down of the blood pigment, haemoglobin, and is then used to digest fats by emulsifying them prior to assimilation into the body. This catabolic activity is related to the fiery element and the activity of the ego (the absorbed fats have the highest calorific value of any substances in the body and can be described as *concentrated heat*). Even so, the liver is the centre of anabolism and vitality in the body, as demonstrated by its remarkable regenerative ability. If three-quarters of the liver is removed, the remaining quarter is capable of adapting to the task of the whole organ and, in time, of growing back to full size.

Health is not merely an expression of strong upbuilding forces but a balance between anabolic and catabolic processes. The pathological danger from an excess of anabolism is that it leads to the storing of more substances than can be broken down for use by the body. If not checked by the catabolic activity of the ego and astral body, the anabolic liver processes can cause a certain heaviness more akin to the earth element. On a very subtle level, this is the basis of depression, when a heavy sluggishness enters into the *watery* processes of the liver. There would not necessarily be any measurable changes in the liver or any physical liver disease — the changes are within the etheric liver rather than the physical organ. However, severe liver diseases such as hepatitis are often followed by depression.

During the regenerative time of sleep, up to about three o'clock in the morning, the liver stores more sugar in the form of glycogen than it breaks down. From three onwards, the balance shifts back in favour of breaking down glycogen, making glucose available to the muscles for bodily activity during the day. It is around this time that many depressives wake up and experience severe mental anguish and restlessness, often finding it impossible to get back to sleep. It is interesting that many of the treatments for depression considered successful by conventional medicine, involve a strengthening of the body's catabolic processes. For example, most antidepressant drugs have a stimulating effect on catabolic amines. In the same vein, depriving people of sleep can, at least temporarily, relieve depression by stopping the building-up processes becoming excessive. Similarly, very strenuous exercise, which increases the burning of glucose in the muscles, can also bring relief.

The other aspect of the liver, the production of bile, is associated with the opposite psychiatric state of mania. This is less common than depression but, when it occurs, often follows it. Whereas the depressive is weighed down, lacking motivation and inactive, the manic has an inner lightness and is bursting with motivation and excessive activity — life seems without boundaries. In the depressive, the normal flow of thoughts becomes sluggish; in the manic, it is accelerated. The mood of the depressive is like stagnant water; that of the manic is overheated.

Obsessional and compulsive illnesses are characterized by a fixed idea or recurrent action that dominates the patient's life. Commonly, these obsessional thoughts are associated with being dirty. For example, the idea that the hands must be dirty after touching something, and that an illness might be passed on to someone, may lead to a compulsion to wash continually. Often the idea is not completely groundless, but is exaggerated out of all proportion. In most cases, patients know that the idea is absurd but are unable to free themselves from it, as if the idea itself had become something solid and could not be dissolved. The fixity of the idea and the patient's inability to escape from it suggests that the solidity of the earthly element is expressed in such a condition.

It might at first appear unlikely that the earth element should have a special connection with the lung, which it would seem natural to link to the element of air. However, although the organ contains air, in its structure we find hard cartilage in the larynx and rings of cartilage forming the air passages. The air breathed into the lungs is separated from the blood by the thinnest of membranes. In this sense, the lung is the one organ where the physical (earth) environment virtually touches the interior of the body. The air breathed in has a cooling effect on the lung, keeping it at a lower temperature than most of the body, and this quality of coolness is also a characteristic of the earth element. Like the heart, the lung is in constant movement but, unlike the heart, its movement is passive. Breathing in is brought about by the expansion of the chest wall and flattening of the diaphragm — the lung's elastic fibres see to it that it passively contracts again to breathe out.

Many illnesses illustrate the lung's particular relationship to the mineral world and its associated susceptibility to hardening processes. They include silicosis, which is caused by inhaling rock dust containing silica, and the miners' lung disease pneumoconiosis. Hardening of the lung often accompanies long-term infections such as recurrent bronchitis or tuberculosis, which brings about the formation of calcified areas. The lung is the key to a healthy relationship between the soul and the earth element. An excessive mineral influence in the soul leads to the fixity of obsessive ideas and compulsive behaviour, whereas a lack gives rise to flights of fancy and a tendency to be *up in the clouds* rather than *down to earth*. Tuberculosis of the lung can produce the latter symptoms. Hospitals which specialized in tuberculosis in the days when it was more common, were known for their euphoric atmospheres, and the illness was a common affliction of gifted artists.

One patient who was treated at Park Attwood Clinic for obsessional, compulsive problems was a 46-year-old man who had first developed symptoms in his late teens. He was obsessively preoccupied with the ageing of his body and would compulsively clean his teeth for hours for fear that they might decay. His obsession with his teeth was part of a general fear that his body was beginning to age and degenerate. He had had psychoanalysis for many years, and could discuss at length his theories on what the symptoms meant and why he had the problem, but this didn't seem to make him any more able to deal with it. He felt that he had never had fun or allowed himself to behave spontaneously in his teens and twenties and thought it was vital to make up for lost time, which he saw in terms of having affairs with younger women. But, in the presence of attractive young women, he found he became very anxious and inhibited. A striking feature of his symptoms, which was not very typical of obsessive behaviour, was that he would become stuck or frozen in the middle of doing something, such as cleaning his teeth or eating in the presence of others, and would be unable to continue. When he had these inhibited phases, he would often withdraw to bed for a day at a time.

He was thin, with a large head and a rather gaunt, bony appearance His skin was pale and wrinkled, and his temperature often as low as 35.5 degrees Celsius. He had a cold laugh, was rather cynical and had a tendency to talk at length about his problems. The coldness, pallor, over-intellectuality, large head and premature ageing point strongly to a preponderant activity of the nerve-sense pole, and his desire for spontaneity and sexual encounters could be seen as an attempt to compensate for this.

With this picture in mind, the aim of treatment was to bring about movement and warmth in his soul to counteract the fixity and coldness. Initially, there was very little counselling or psychotherapy and the emphasis was on physical treatments and artistic therapies. He was given a number of medicines which have a particular relationship to the lung or to the rhythmic system in general, eurythmy therapy and painting therapy. For the deep-seated coldness, he was given viscum treatment (see Chapter 13) and pyrogenic baths (see Chapter 8), a combination which had a dramatic effect. Immediately after the baths, when he appeared flushed, he was markedly less fixed in his behaviour, and his social contacts became more relaxed and natural. He began to notice that his feet and hands were generally warmer and his body temperature rose to about 36 degrees. Although his obsessional problems did not disappear, they became less frequent and less severe. Despite having found it very difficult at first to relate to the painting therapy while at Park Attwood, he later decided to pursue it as a long-term therapy. Ten years after the initial treatment, he was largely free from his obsessive problems and, looking back, felt that the medicines and baths had been especially beneficial.

The organ which has a special relationship to the airy element and the astral body is the kidney. The outer layer of the kidney contains minute, cup-shaped structures called glomeruli which begin the process of urine production. They are remarkable in that they not only have an oxygen-rich blood supply entering them via an artery, but also oxygen-rich blood leaving them again through a small artery. This double arterial connection is the opposite of the double venous connection found in the liver. The venous blood has a relatively low pressure and is slower moving. It is also rich in carbon dioxides indicating its association with the etheric body and the plant realm. The arterial supply has a powerful pulse and is rich in the oxygen needed for the combustion of sugars, indicating its association with the astral body and the animal realm. This association is reinforced by the effects of the two hormones produced by the kidney; erythropoietin and renin. The former increases the oxygen-carrying capacity of the blood, and renin stimulates the production of angiotensin, which is thought to maintain arterial blood pressure. The kidney function is dependent on a certain blood pressure being maintained, and kidney failure is one of the consequences if it falls below the minimum, as it can in cases of prolonged shock.

The strong relationship of the kidney to the astral body, and to psychiatric disorders, is even more apparent if the adrenal gland, which sits on the kidney, is brought into the picture. The central part of this gland comprises cells that are derived from nervous tissue. They produce adrenaline at times of stress, resulting in many of the symptoms of fear, such as a racing heart, trembling, and coolness in the peripheral parts of the body. The outer part of the adrenal gland produces steroids, which also have a relationship to stress in that part of their function appears to be protecting the body from the excesses of stress reactions. The sex hormones are chemically related to steroids, and the reproductive organs are themselves embryologically related to the kidney system. The anthroposophical concept of the kidney goes far beyond the physical organ and includes the spiritual activity associated with it, the adrenal glands and, to some extent, the reproductive organs as well. Similarly, the concept of the liver encompasses the totality of the anabolic processes in the body which, though concentrated in the liver, are by no means limited to that physical organ.

The kidney's association with the astral body makes it come to mind when a patient presents severe symptoms of anxiety and agitation. Anxiety, a psychiatric problem in its own right, is a very common disorder which often colours depression and is frequently found to be an element in schizophrenia. The patient in her mid-thirties described in Chapter 4 was suffering from depression and had marked symptoms of anxiety. She had great difficulty sleeping and the lower half of her body was extremely cold. With the kidney specifically in mind, copper ointment was applied over the kidney region and a homeopathic preparation of naturally occurring copper oxide, Cuprite D6, was given orally.[1] She also had mustard footbaths and oil-dispersion baths with lavender and arnica for the coldness. To strengthen the reproductive organs, she was given a mixture of herbs called Menodoron (see Chapter 14) and injections of Argentite D10 (silver ore) under the skin. Her depression was treated with a liver medicine, Stannum per Taraxicum (tin potentized using dandelion).

At first, the main emphasis was on these medical treatments, although her anxiety was initially so extreme that, for a time, she also needed conventional sedatives. Later, she progressed to therapies such as eurythmy and painting. In the latter, she had an experience which she found to be very therapeutic when working on a series of paintings consisting of sunset, night sky and various stages of sunrise. The transition from light to darkness was accompanied by a letting go of her fixed ideas about herself. The gradual return to light through the stages of sunrise brought with it an increasing sense of identity and self-worth. Her recovery from the severe anxiety and depression proved to be an important turning-point in her life.[2]

Just as the astral body has a special connection with the kidney, the ego is associated with the heart. The ego often has to resolve inner conflicts when, for example, instinctive drives are found to be incompatible with personal ideals. In this sense, the ego tries to harmonize the opposing elements in the soul — the instinctive drives associated with the unconscious metabolic pole, and the ideals associated with the conscious reasoning of the head pole. The heart has the comparable role of harmonizing the physical activity of the two poles in the body.

The heart is the central organ of the rhythmic system and is positioned within the chest cavity, where the head and metabolic poles meet. It fills on expansion (diastole) and empties on contraction (systole), setting up a rhythmic pulse. It is also the central point of the circulation — blood flows from the whole body towards the heart, then to the lungs and back to the heart, before flowing out to all parts of the body again. The rhythmic system as a whole is associated with feelings, and the heart is the traditional symbol of love.

The natural element associated with the ego and the heart is fire. The ego gives us a continuing sense of identity, despite the soul's changing thoughts, emotions and urges. It carries responsibility for our actions and steers our course through life, and in this sense is responsible for both the past and future. Two faculties that are characteristic of the human ego reflect this — conscience and courage. In so far as we are aware of a responsibility for the past, this is carried within us as conscience, while it takes moral courage to face the future.

It is perhaps connected with the fact that the spirit itself cannot be ill that the heart does not give rise to a specific psychiatric illness, as do the kidney, liver and lung. Rather, it colours the illnesses of the other three organs, when the two faculties of conscience and courage become distorted. Conscience should be a spur to learn from past mistakes but, if someone is totally weighed down by guilt over past actions, this becomes harmful. Guilt can be seen as pathological distortion of conscience and, although it is not recognized as a psychiatric illness in its own right, it can be a major factor in illnesses such as depression.

The other faculty, courage, which gives us the strength to strive onward into the future, is lost in severe depression when patients can be so bound up with the past that they cannot relate to the future at all. Courage may then be expressed in a distorted, destructive way in rage, when the will to act is overpowering and beyond the ego's control. Rage and violent outbursts sometimes feature in mania and catatonic schizophrenia, but they can also be a problem in everyday life without being symptoms of a psychiatric illness. Some people are prone to swing between rage and deep guilt for what they have done, and this points particularly to a need for the moderating and harmonizing qualities of the ego and the heart.

Treatment of psychiatric symptoms which point to the heart includes medicines such as homeopathically prepared gold (aurum) and Onopordon comp., a mixture of *Onopordon acanthium* (cotton thistle), *Hyoscyamus niger* (henbane), and *Primula officinalis* (cowslip). This combination represents a harmonious balance of catabolic and anabolic forces. Artistic therapies can also be used to support the rhythmic system and to help restore a proper balance between the two poles. Therapeutic massage, too, may be used to reinforce the heart's harmonizing activity. Such therapies would accompany treatment aimed at the other main organ involved. For example, if severe guilt formed part of a patient's depression, the heart would be treated as well as the liver.

Some drugs are able to produce dramatic psychological effects through their direct biochemical action on the physical organs. The effects vary with different drugs but anthroposophical doctors consider that they all affect the total constitution — ego, astral body, etheric body and physical body. Amphetamines (or speed) produce rapid thinking and hyperactivity but damage the etheric body, leading to a lack of vitality and will power. LSD gives rise to powerful hallucinations which are caused by a slight separation of the etheric body from the physical body. Marijuana has a similar but less extreme effect. Heroin completely blocks out any sense of guilt or shame. It dislocates the ego from the rest of the constitution, causing the astral body to be dominated by instinctive desires. Addiction can remove any sense of conscience, with the whole life revolving around getting the next 'fix.'

Human Element	Natural Element	Organ	Psychiatric symptom
Ego	Fire	Heart (and gall bladder)	Rage, guilt (and mania)
Astral Body	Air	Kidney	Anxiety
Etheric Body	Water	Liver	Depression
Physical Body	Earth	Lung	Obsession

Figure 10.

A healthy path of inner development eventually leads to powerful experiences of the spiritual realms, including perception of the etheric and astral forces at work within oneself. In this sense, deeper self-knowledge is a prerequisite for true spiritual perception, however painful it might be. Becoming conscious of the astral forces within one's soul is usually a frightening experience, even for someone who is well-prepared. If it is brought about without proper preparation, it can be shattering. Initially, the experiences produced by taking LSD can seem wonderful but, sooner or later, a 'bad trip' occurs, when these inner astral forces are directly confronted.

There are two anthroposophical centres for treating drug addiction, one in Germany, called Zeiben Zwerge, and the other, called Arta, in the Netherlands (*see* Section 2 of Contact Addresses). Co-workers at Arta have found that it is rare for addicts to take the decision to 'kick the habit' before the age of twenty-one, roughly the age at which the forces of the ego become partially freed from their unconscious activity. Treatment is based on the conception that the addict's whole constitution is damaged by the drug abuse The phases of childhood described in Chapter 10 show how the etheric body, astral body and ego are emancipated at the end of each of the seven-year periods. At Arta, the treatment programme is based on a recapitulation of these phases in order to rebuild each of the constitutional elements. Also, it has been found that the medical and therapeutic work must be combined with social support to be successful — neither approach is sufficient on its own.

The first phase of treatment focuses on the physical body with the physical withdrawal from use of the drugs. This is undertaken on small farms or smallholdings where five co-workers live and work with seven addicts, who are referred to as residents. They have a strict, rhythmic timetable and there is an emphasis on physical nutrition and work. They have a balanced wholefood diet and regular times when they do gardening or work with animals. This phase usually lasts about seven weeks, during which they are given a great deal of guidance and support by the co-workers.

The second phase puts the emphasis on emotional nutrition. The residents move into the main building at Arta where they live as a community, again with a number of co-workers. They are still prevented from leaving the centre or obtaining drugs. There is a strong emphasis on all kinds of artistic activity, group discussions and much personal conversation. All residents are involved in the household chores to reawaken an awareness of the practical necessities of everyday life. There is an environment of cultural nutrition similar to that which should be provided by school for the child in the seven to fourteen phase, and there is still plenty of guidance from co-workers.

Having spent some time without drugs, the residents find that they become more emotionally vulnerable, as their feelings are no longer suppressed by the drug taking. Very often, it turns out that they were emotionally and culturally deprived in childhood, and this period can be of great benefit to them by providing the cultural enrichment and emotional support that they have always lacked. Although they are likely to be receiving anthroposophical medication and therapies during this stage, the main emphasis is on group experience. Most of the therapeutic artistic and practical activities are performed all together.

In the next stage, which relates to the fourteen to twenty-one phase, the emphasis shifts to individual responsibility and independence. Each resident now has weekly conversations with a counsellor, and the therapies used become directed to their individual needs. Having to make decisions again, residents often feel they are back where they were before they started to take drugs. The fourth stage, relating to the twenty-one to twenty-eight phase, is entered only after the resident has been at the centre for at least twelve months. Leaving the premises unescorted is now allowed and residents handle their money for themselves. They take work or training placements outside Arta and assume a certain amount of responsibility for newcomers at the centre.

While the various stages form a framework for the programme at Arta, they are not a fixed, rigid structure. The programme tries to take account of the individual needs of the resident as a person with a soul and a spirit, rather than treating the problem purely as inappropriate behaviour, as do addiction centres based on behavioural therapy. Typically, behavioural therapy centres have success rates of between ten and fifteen per cent, whereas Arta, with its more comprehensive approach, is able to report a fifty-two per cent success rate.

As has been seen, when treating illnesses with physical symptoms, anthroposophical doctors look for the cause in the astral body and ego so that they may deal with that as well as the physical symptoms themselves. In the same way, treatment of illnesses with mental and emotional symptoms is based on an understanding of the related disorders of the physical and etheric bodily processes.

13. Immunity, Aids and Cancer

The immune system protects the physical body from invading organisms and harmful substances. It helps to ensure that the body's life processes remain dominant and are not hindered by the foreign processes of other organisms. The most obvious barrier to the outside world is the skin, but the lining of the gut and the airways of the nose and lungs also act as barriers when food or air are taken into the body. These are complemented by the immune system, which recognizes foreign substances inside the body and activates processes to render them harmless or destroy them.

The recognition of what is *foreign* to the body requires the ability to distinguish between human and animal, plant or mineral substances, and also between its own body and other human material. The immune processes are not only guardians of the human organism, but also an expression of the unique identity of each person. In this sense, they are connected with the activity of the ego. Two major illnesses are related to the immune system — Aids (acquired immune deficiency syndrome) and cancer. In Aids, immunity breaks down, leaving the body vulnerable to massive infections of a sort not usually experienced by humans. In cancer, normal cells start behaving as if they were foreign to the organism and undermine the body from within.

Of the outer barriers to foreign substances, the skin is very effective against viruses and bacteria and is breached only when an area has been damaged or weakened. Even the human immunodeficiency virus (HIV), which causes Aids, cannot invade the body if the skin and related boundary structures remain intact. Although it does not need to be able to sense foreign forms of life, the skin has many qualities related to the nerve-sense processes of the body. It is sensitive to temperature, touch and pain, and for this reason is rightly regarded as an extensive sense organ. It also expresses the individual's identity in the sense that its markings, such as fingerprints, are unique to each person.

The breaking-down effect of nerve-sense activity and its opposite, the upbuilding of the metabolic system, form a duality which can be described as the death forces (nerve-sense) on the one hand, and the life forces (metabolic) on the other. The deadening physical effect of nerve-sense activity plays an essential part in the function of the skin. In the deeper layers, which are in close contact with the blood capillaries, skin cells rapidly reproduce. The new cells migrate upwards, gradually losing their rounded shape and their capacity to divide. They become flattened and the cytoplasm (the part of the cell surrounding the nucleus) fills with a protein called keratin. This hardens the cells and, as they die on reaching the outermost layers, they remain hard, with the keratin within them. These cells provide a tough barrier to the outer world and the dead, keratin-filled layers become particularly thick where the skin is exposed to constant abrasion, such as on the soles of the feet.

The health of the skin depends on the maintenance of a proper balance between the vital reproductive activity of the deeper layers and the deadening nearer the surface. Many skin problems, such as eczema, result from these two processes falling out of balance. When the metabolic (life) processes predominate, the inflammatory, wet phase of eczema occurs. It is in this phase that the skin can become infected because there is no longer a protective layer of hardened cells. In the dry, scaly phase of eczema, the nerve-sense (death) processes are predominant. Other moist, protective surfaces, such as those lining the gut and parts of the genitals, also have a reproductive layer and a progressive differentiation of the cells as they migrate towards the surface, but without the production of a final horny, keratinized outer layer. When this deadening process fails to occur, and the migrating cells retain their ability to reproduce, there is an increased risk of cancer. It is the detection of a loss of this differentiation in the outer layers of cells that underlies cervical smear screening, enabling treatment to be given before malignant changes take place.

The skin provides what is called a non-specific defence against substances outside. Another aspect of non-specific immunity is the ability to develop high fevers. An increase in body temperature from 37 degrees Celsius to 39 degrees is sufficient to kill a number of foreign micro-organisms and also stimulates the rest of the immune system. The white blood cells, capable of engulfing and digesting bacteria and viruses, add a third line of defence. These cells (neutrophils and macrophages) are able to migrate out of the blood vessels and are often found close to the skin and other protective surfaces. They are capable of attacking micro-organisms whether they have encountered them before or not, but they are not as effective at killing viruses as a fourth element of the immune system, called acquired immunity, which has to be developed to combat specific viruses.

Several types of white blood cells called lymphocytes are particularly involved in acquired immunity. For example, B-lymphocytes produce antibodies against specific micro-organisms and the poisons they create, whereas T-lymphocytes (so-called because they mature in the thymus) kill foreign organisms directly and also stimulate the production of more B-lymphocytes. The responses of these cells are geared to the unique chemical composition of the invading micro-organisms. Once the infection has been dealt with, a small number of cells specifically adapted to fight that type of micro-organism remain as a kind of memory. On further infection, they help to produce specific T-cells much more quickly, and the body is then said to be immune to that particular illness.

The way the white blood cells engulf and digest the foreign micro-organisms is closely related to the catabolic processes in the digestion of food. Similar enzymes are produced to do the breaking down in each case. The white cells' ability to 'sense' foreign substances also relates their activity to the catabolic nerve-sense system. Recent discoveries have shown that the immune system can be stimulated or inhibited by the nervous system, and the relationship can also work the other way. The lymphocytes can themselves influence the nervous system by, for example, inducing sleep. The immune and nervous systems and the production of hormones are now seen to be so closely interrelated that they are often referred to as the neuro-immuno-endocrine system.

The white blood cells with the central function of searching for invading micro-organisms and initiating the development of cells to produce antibodies are the T-lymphocytes, and they are the key to overcoming new types of infection. It is these T-cells that are attacked and destroyed by the human immunodeficiency virus (HIV). The virus insinuates itself into a host cell's genetic material and remains dormant until another virus stimulates the infected T-cell to multiply itself. Instead of reproducing itself, it creates large numbers of new HIVs which are released into the blood as the T-cell dies. They are attracted to T-cells, and also to other white blood cells and nerve cells, so the process is then repeated on a larger scale. Another effect of the HIV is to cause as many as fifty T-cells to fuse together, rendering them inactive. The virus avoids complete destruction by antibodies by regularly changing the chemical composition of its protein coat. This makes a second HIV infection invulnerable to the large numbers of antibodies produced in response to the first infection. Not only is it therefore impossible to become immune to the HIV, but a latent tendency to develop Aids may be triggered in an infected patient when the T-cells attempt to multiply to deal with a later infection, leading to the production of further HIVs.

Outside the body, the HIV is quite fragile and is easily destroyed. It cannot penetrate the skin, and infection is transmitted only by an exchange of body fluids. At the time of writing, it was known that it could be passed on by infected blood, semen or vaginal fluid. The main ways this has happened are through sexual intercourse, when body fluids have passed from one person to another via small cuts or abrasions, through the sharing of needles by addicts injecting drugs intravenously, from the blood of an infected mother to her unborn baby, and through blood transfusions, which took place before it was known that this could transmit the virus.

The main result of HIV infection is a marked depletion in the number of T-cells. In an attempt to compensate, the B-cells become hyperactive, but the antibodies they make are incapable of destroying the HIV. Antibodies are produced which would defend the body against all the infections previously encountered but, because of the deficiency of T-cells, the body remains vulnerable to new infections. This means that HIV-positive adults keep their immunity to common human infections but become susceptible to animal viruses. They might get pneumonia from *Pneumocystis carinii,* which normally infects rats, or another form of pneumonia from *Mycobacterium avium,* which causes tuberculosis in birds. They are also vulnerable to parasitic micro-organisms that normally live on cats, dogs and cattle. In addition to this, infections which are normally localized, such as thrush (a common infection of the mouth in children and the vagina in adults), can become rampant throughout the gastro-intestinal tract.

HIV infection may remain dormant for some time, but when it progresses to the point when the immune system breaks down the patient is said to have developed Aids. Rampant infections can then have a very debilitating effect on the body. The areas that may become infected include the mouth, the gut, the lungs with various forms of pneumonia, and the skin — in other words, all the boundaries of the body are attacked. In its interference with the genetic material of T-cells, the HIV attacks perhaps the most physical expression of human individuality. An Aids patient has short periods of fever, which are quite different from the sustained high fevers of other infections. Unlike the sustained fever, which is part of a healing process, they are chaotic, indicating the inability of the ego to bring about a healing effect through the medium of warmth. Perhaps as a result of the infection of the nervous system, or perhaps because of exhaustion, in the latter stages of the illness, Aids patients have poor concentration and weakened short-term memory. This again indicates interference with the activity of the ego, as does the inability of patients to express themselves through gestures or facial expressions, which tend to become blank.

These phenomena indicate that the HIV destroys the body's ability to be a suitable vehicle for the ego, or spirit. It is expressed most acutely in the killing of the T-cells, which normally play the key role in distinguishing self from non-self when encountering new infections. This marks out the HIV as a destroyer of the physical guardian of the human identity — the immune system. Not only does it interfere with the ego's activity in the body, but it also makes the body vulnerable to attack by a multitude of diseases that would normally be found only in animals.

As described in Chapter 2, cancer occurs when cells in a part of the body stop limiting their growth in accordance with the normal behaviour of the tissue concerned. When the growth reaches the point when it breaks through the boundaries of the tissues in which it originated, this is taken as a sign of malignancy. It may then leave the organ of origin and travel around the body via the blood or other fluids to form further tumours called metastases. In remaining relatively undifferentiated and reproducing without restraint, the cancerous cells behave more like isolated cells living in a nutrient medium outside the body than as integrated parts of a complex organism.

About ninety-five per cent of all malignant tumours arise in surface tissue, such as the skin, the lining of the gut, and the linings of glands like the breasts. The remaining five per cent mainly originate in the muscles, bones and blood vessels. Much research has been done into cellular changes in the surface tissues, which may be intermediate stages between healthy tissues and malignant growths. In the case of the cervix (the neck of the womb) the tissue layers are similar to those in skin, except that the uppermost layers do not become as hard, although the cells do flatten and stop reproducing as they migrate upwards. Under normal circumstances, the nuclei gradually shrink as the cells migrate. By the time they reach the surface, the nuclei have disappeared and the cells are completely flat.

When this process breaks down, the cells retain their large nuclei and their ability to divide as they migrate. While these cells remain in the original tissue, it is not yet cancer, but there is a far greater risk of cancer developing. The basal layer of cells rests on a thin membrane. If this membrane is breached by the cells, this is an indication that cancer has developed. Similar changes to these are thought to take place prior to malignant tumours arising in other tissues, such as the lining of the large bowel, which is a common site of cancer.

It can be seen that a first stage leading to the possible development of cancer occurs when cells retain their reproductive ability and do not undergo a process of differentiation as they migrate through the layers of protective tissue. They retain their vitality and do not undergo a death process. In the next stage, when the tumour becomes malignant, it has to develop its own blood circulation to continue living and growing beyond a few millimetres across. It has been found that the tumours are able to attract the development of blood capillaries from outside the tissue of origin so that these grow into the tumour. This enables further, much larger growth to take place and, later, cells from the tumour might break away and give rise to further growths elsewhere in the body.

Anthroposophical medicine sees the life processes originating in the etheric body as expansive, undifferentiated growth activity. But the human form is imposed upon that activity by the ego, working through the astral body into the etheric body. This exerts a limiting effect on what would otherwise be formless growth. Differentiated growth — in which the cells change form as they divide to follow the human template — requires that the tendency of the cells to reproduce towards formless growth is held in check.

In the pre-cancerous stage, the form-giving death process breaks down. Cancer arises when the tumour breaches the boundaries of the original tissue. So, from an anthroposophical view, cancer represents the autonomous working of the etheric and physical bodies, without the controlling influence of the ego, which bears the human image. The therapeutic aim, therefore, is to find ways of stimulating the form-giving activity of the ego so that it regains mastery over the growth processes. The plant mistletoe *(Viscum album)* displays certain unique features which indicate its suitability for this task.

Mistletoe is semi-parasitic, growing on trees and drawing water and minerals from its host. Like other green plants, it is capable of photosynthesis but, in contrast, it is unable to transport sugars and has chlorophyll spread throughout its tissues, enabling it to synthesize sugars wherever they are needed. Its leaves have a simple form which changes very little during growth, and, unlike most leaves, have no difference between their upper and lower surfaces. These characteristics suggest a relatively undifferentiated nature, and this is found again in the flowers, which are so uninteresting that it is difficult to imagine how insects are attracted to pollinate the plant. Even the seeds within the familiar white translucent berries are relatively undifferentiated and, deprived of the light which passes through the berries, the seeds die within a few days.

The majority of plants respond to gravity by the upper part growing vertically into a main stem, with branches growing from it. This is evident from the first shoots, with the primary leaf always growing upwards, and the first root downwards, irrespective of how the seed lies in the ground. The mistletoe grows spherically from where it is attached to the host tree. Initially the stems grow vertically but, once established, they spread in all directions, as if the plant withdraws from any relationship to gravity. Mistletoe is also inhibited with respect to time. Unlike most plants, it begins to develop the organs of its flowers at the same time as its leaves, but the flower itself does not appear until the third year. Its cycles of activity are so slowed that the rhythm of the seasons has little influence on it. These rather primitive qualities and the way the mistletoe holds back from taking on a more specialized form are reminiscent of the way the human formative forces also hold back from specialization to retain versatility (see Chapter 2). It is this human formative principle that is weakened in cancer. The fact that mistletoe holds back its own development so strongly suggests that it may strengthen this characteristically human formative principle, and offer an effective treatment for cancer.

Medicinal preparations of mistletoe for treating cancer were first made in the 1920s following suggestions by Steiner. They have since been developed by six different companies. The most well known of the current remedies is Iscador, manufactured by the Hiscia Institute at Arlesheim, in Switzerland. A considerable body of scientific literature exists documenting its laboratory testing and clinical use in treating cancer patients. Research has shown that mistletoe preparations stimulate the growth of the thymus gland, where the T-cells develop. It has also been shown to stimulate the production of antibodies when the organism faces injected foreign material. Of the immune processes that are known to natural science, many are directly influenced by mistletoe treatment. As the remedy is damaged by exposure to the digestive juices, it is administered by injection under the skin. This often causes a slight rise in temperature, which is welcomed as an additional stimulus to the immune system.

There are more than twenty-five clinical studies of the use of

mistletoe preparations in the treatment of twelve different types
of malignant tumour. They were not double-blind trials, the standard method used by conventional medicine, but the results were
nevertheless very encouraging. There is no suggestion that the
current remedies are miracle cures, but they do appear to prolong
life and reduce the risk of the cancer spreading. They are also free
from the very unpleasant side effects of most conventional cancer
drugs.

Although there is some evidence of a unique anti-tumour action, their main effect is to mobilize and strengthen aspects of the
patient's immune system so that it is better able to oppose the cancer itself. They can be used alongside conventional treatments
such as surgery, radiotherapy and chemotherapy, and there is
some evidence that they help patients to withstand the damaging
effects of these forms of treatment. Research has shown that the
part of the bone marrow which produces red blood cells, and
which is impaired by radiotherapy, recovers more quickly following previous treatment with a mistletoe preparation.[1] The effectiveness of mistletoe treatment can be enhanced, and the
form-giving activity of the ego further supported, by eurythmy
therapy, artistic therapies and hydrotherapy.

It has been seen that, in Aids, there is a similar breakdown in
the processes through which the ego maintains its stamp of identity on the body. The characteristics of the illness, such as the attack on the T-cells rendering them ineffective, suggest that the
special properties of mistletoe might also be beneficial in the
treatment of Aids. At the time of writing, experimental treatment
was under way, and clinical trials were planned.

14. The Medicines

At the heart of anthroposophical medicine lies the doctor's extended view of illness, and the natural substances which can be used as remedies. The preparation of a medicine is just as important as the choice of the substance itself. Methods of preparation are used which are designed to accentuate the substance's therapeutic properties, and anthroposophical doctors work in close collaboration with pharmacists to develop appropriate methods. Traditional pharmaceutical and homeopathic techniques are used, but new methods have also been introduced as a result of this collaboration.

Great care is always taken in collecting and harvesting raw materials — whether animal, plant or mineral. When plants need to be cultivated, rather than gathered from the wild, they are grown using the methods of biodynamic farming and gardening. This is a development of organic practice which uses anthroposophical knowledge of the relationship between spirit and matter to strengthen the growth of plants and animals. Biodynamic farming and gardening is free from additives, hormones and chemicals, and makes beneficial use of the effects of the natural cycles of the sun, the moon and the seasons.[1]

One of the new pharmaceutical processes is a development of the homeopathic principle of potentization, through which the non-physical qualities of a substance are released to be used therapeutically. In homeopathic potentization, a small quantity of the material is repeatedly dissolved in water, or alcohol and water, and is succussed (vigorously shaken) for a prescribed period at each stage of the dilution. Steiner suggested that the process could be aided by having plants absorb the materials to be potentized. The substance is introduced into the soil in which given plants are growing. These are later harvested and composted, and a second generation of plants is grown on the composted material. The process is repeated, and the third generation is used to prepare a medicine.

Anthroposophical pharmacy also makes use of selected temperatures in the preparation of medicines. In classical homeopathic pharmacy, medicines are made from plants by finely chopping the material and mixing it with alcohol and water. The mixture is allowed to stand in temperatures below 20 degrees Celsius for at least five days before being filtered. This produces the mother tincture which is used to start the process of potentization.

In anthroposophical practice, the temperature of preparation is varied according to the particular medicine Aconite, which bears qualities of coldness allied to the head forces, is prepared at a cool temperature. By contrast, birch leaves, which are used to overcome hardening and sclerosis, are prepared at around 90 degrees. Medicines with a particular affinity to the middle, rhythmic system — such as crataegus, which strengthens the heart — are prepared at the mean human temperature of about 37 degrees. The link between warmth and the ego has already been described and, in this sense, the attention paid to the temperature of preparation can be seen as helping to relate the medicines specifically to humans. Cooking food and using fire are exclusively human activities, and cooked food is considered to be more fit for humans to eat.

As was seen in the previous chapter, the special qualities of mistletoe make it suitable for treating illnesses in which the stamp of human identity is lost, such as cancer and Aids. But a very complex method of preparation is required, involving mixing winter and summer sap by adding drops of one to a fine film of the other on a rapidly spinning disc. There is also a controlled fermentation process. At least three research institutes are working independently on optimizing a method of preparing mistletoe extracts for treating cancer, based on indications given in 1920 by Steiner. In 1990, it emerged that at least one method produced a medicine containing lectins, a group of substances which are thought by immunologists to stimulate the appropriate immune responses in the body. There is also some evidence that lectins are found in relatively higher concentrations in the higher potencies of mistletoe (i.e. more diluted). It is thought that they are less stable in the lower potencies and degenerate more rapidly. Although the special techniques for preparing mistletoe have involved considerable technology, most of the methods of anthroposophical pharmacy are more akin to those of traditional pharmacy, and are often done by hand.

The development of anthroposophical pharmacy began with a single pharmacist, Otto Schmiedel, working in Arlesheim, Switzerland, next door to the clinic where Ita Wegman and Rudolf Steiner were collaborating on the founding of anthroposophical medicine. The laboratory he set up grew into the medicines manufacturer, Weleda, which now has branches in twenty-six countries around the world. These branches make the majority of the medicines from plants gathered in their own countries. For example, Weleda (UK) Limited, at Ilkeston in England, has its own extensive herb gardens where many of the medicinal substances are grown.

The work of Rudolf Hauschka, who developed methods of preparation of medicines which avoided the use of alcohol, led to the establishment of a second anthroposophical pharmaceutical company, Wala. This is based at Eckwalden, in southern Germany, and its products are distributed worldwide. The development of mistletoe preparations for the treatment of cancer was pioneered by the Hiscia Institute in Switzerland, which makes the most widely known medicine, Iscador. At the time of writing, Iscador was the only mistletoe preparation licensed in the UK. Two newer research institutes, Abnoba and Helixor, have developed their own cancer medicines from mistletoe. These are licensed in Germany and marketed as Viscum Abnoba and Helixor.

Often, an anthroposophical doctor's prescription is highly individualized to reflect the particular spiritual and physical constitution of the patient. This is particularly likely to be the case when homeopathically potentized metals are given. However, in certain disorders, the prescription is specific to the particular illness or symptoms. For example, Combudoron is a combination of arnica and urtica designed for the treatment of burns, and Avena Sativa comp. is a mixture of herbal and homeopathically prepared ingredients put together specifically to help in cases of sleeplessness. A number of the medicines designed for specific illnesses and symptoms could be prescribed by any doctor, without detailed knowledge of anthroposophical medicine. In Central Europe, where doctors are more open to the use of natural medicines, many do just that. Some of these medicines are also safe to be sold over the counter to patients who treat themselves without consulting a doctor.

Many small accidents and minor illnesses can be treated that way. Patients are encouraged by conventional doctors and drug companies to use aspirins or cough medicines on their own, and anthroposophical physicians can similarly recommend a number of medicines as household remedies. The following is a selection of such remedies, which could make up a very useful home medicine chest.

Unless otherwise stated, the medicines should be taken at least twenty minutes before or after meals or drinks, if possible. Pills should be dissolved in the mouth rather than swallowed whole.

Amara drops
Mixture of herbal bitters, including gentian (Gentiana lutea), chicory (Chicorium intybus), wormwood (Artemisia absinthium) and yarrow (Achillea millefolium).

Use to treat nausea and to improve poor appetite. Take fifteen drops in very little water every few hours (nausea), or about twenty minutes before food (lack of appetite).

Arnica
Homeopathic potency of leopard's bane (Arnica montana).

Use in potency D6 (also called 6x) following shock, either physical or emotional. One tablet every hour.

Arnica lotion
For external use, one dessertspoon in half a pint of water to make compresses for treating sprains and bruises.

Arnica ointment
Can also be used externally for sprains and bruises. Massage well into the affected area twice daily or as required.

Avena Sativa comp.
Mixture of common valerian (Valeriana officinalis) passion flower (Passiflora incarnata), hops, oats and a high homeopathic potency of coffee.

Use for insomnia, particularly when caused by nervous restlessness. Twenty to thirty drops in a little water, half an hour before bed.

Balsamicum ointment
Contains marigold (calendula), dog's mercury (Mercurialis perennis), Peru balsam-tree (Myroxylon peruiferum) and antimony (stibium).

A general ointment for wounds. Particularly useful for poorly-healing wounds and infected spots and boils. Can also be used for treating certain forms of eczema and dermatitis. Apply to the affected area directly, or on a dry dressing, two or three times a day.

Bidor
Iron sulphate (ferrous sulphate) and quartz (silica).

For the prevention or treatment of migraine and tension headaches, and the nausea that may accompany them. Bidor's action is directed at harmonizing the fundamental imbalance of the nervous and metabolic systems, which is at the root of the headache, rather than acting as a painkiller. It has none of the side effects which can accompany the use of painkillers and other conventional anti-migraine medication. Treatment is often required to continue for some time to be fully effective.

To prevent migraine attacks, Bidor 1%, one tablet daily for three months. During an attack, Bidor 5%, one or two tablets every half-hour or hour until symptoms are relieved, up to a maximum of twenty tablets in a 12-hour period. The tablets are swallowed whole with water.

Calendula ointment and lotion
Prepared from an alcoholic extract of marigold (calendula).

Useful for minor abrasions, nappy rash, sore nipples and dry eczema. The ointment is applied at least twice a day, either directly to the skin or on a dry dressing. The lotion is diluted in boiled water which has cooled, one teaspoon to a glass of water. It is useful as a soak for skin infections and poorly-healing wounds. May also be used as a compress on a dressing for wet or infected eczema, or for other areas of infected skin which cannot easily be held under water.

Camomile root
A homeopathic potency of camomile root (Matricaria chamomilla).

Particularly useful for treating children's teething pains. Use in potency D3 (also called 3x), two drops in a little water, or two pills, hourly as required. For babies, the pills may be dissolved in a teaspoon of water. Also useful for abdominal cramps, whether associated with stomach upsets and diarrhoea or with cramp-like period pains. Ten drops in a little water, or five pills, every two to three hours until symptoms subside.

Camomile tea
Dried camomile flowers.

For cramp-like pains, from upset stomach or from period pains. Also useful in supporting the treatment of cystitis, when it can be very soothing as well as helping to provide the necessary large fluid intake. Add a half-teaspoon of flowers to a half-pint of boiling water and strain after three minutes. Drink a mugful every few hours, without milk or sugar.

Carvon tablets
Mixture of birch charcoal (Carbo betulae) and caraway seed oil.

For flatulence. Take one to two tablets straight after meals.

Cinnabar/Pyrites
A naturally occurring oxide of mercury (cinnabar) in homeopathic potency D20 and iron sulphide (pyrites) in potency D3.

For sore throats. Dissolve one tablet in the mouth, up to five times a day.

Combudoron ointment and lotion

Combination of leopard's bane (Arnica montana) and the small nettle (Urtica urens).

Designed for the treatment of burns. Has been found to be most valuable for first and second-degree burns, scalds, sunburn, inflamed insect bites and wasp stings. The lotion is diluted in water, approximately one part to ten, for bathing or compresses. It should be applied as soon as possible after a burn and regularly thereafter for a few days. In minor cases, the ointment applied locally may be more convenient.

Copper ointment

Promotes the circulation in hands and feet when coldness is noted. Massage well in, twice a day. Care should be taken as the ointment can mark fabrics — an old pair of socks might prove useful when treating the feet.

Cough elixir

Contains extracts of aniseed (Pimpinella anisum), marsh-mallow root (Althaea officinalis), white horehound (Marrubium vulgare) and thyme (Thymus vulgaris), and homeopathic potencies of sundew (drosera), Brazil root (Cephaelis ipecacuanha) and pasque flower (Pulsatilla vulgaris).

Soothing expectorant for coughs, especially when caused by head colds. One teaspoon every three hours, either neat or in a little water.

Massage balm

Contains leopard's bane (Arnica montana), lavender, rosemary and an extract of birch leaf.

Useful in the treatment of a wide range of conditions involving muscular pains and cramps. Massage well into the affected area twice daily or as required.

Plantago comp. ointment

Contains an extract of great plantain (plantago) and camphor.

For treating coughs and bronchitis, especially in children. Massage on to the chest in the morning and last thing at night.

Not suitable for children under three without medical advice because of the camphor content.

Sage pastilles
Contain extracts of sage and other herbs.

For mild sore throats and dryness and irritation of the throat. Dissolve one in the mouth every one to two hours while symptoms persist.

Silicea comp.
Contains homeopathic potencies of silica (quartz), deadly night-shade (Atropa belladonna) and silver nitrate (argentum nitricum).

For sinusitis, both acute and chronic. May be used in conjunction with inhalations such as eucalyptus oil in hot water. Five pills should be taken, four times a day. If symptoms persist, medical supervision may be necessary.

The above medicines can be prescribed by any doctor, including general practitioners if they are open to using remedies other than conventional drugs. The medicines can also be used safely as home remedies. Those in the following list can also be prescribed by any doctor, but they are not suitable as home remedies because they are for conditions that must be treated by a doctor, or because, under existing regulations in the UK, they are available only on a doctor's prescription (indicated by POM — Prescription-Only Medicine).[2]

Apis/Belladonna
Also called Erysidoron 1. Contains homeopathic potencies of honey-bee poison (Apis mellifica) and deadly nightshade (Atropa belladonna).

For acute local infections, particularly when there is redness and fever, as in acute tonsillitis, boils and mastitis. The dosage is five drops in water every two to three hours during the acute phase. It is sometimes given in hourly alternations with Carbo Betulae 5%/ Sulphur 1% tablets (formerly known as Erysidoron II). Prescribed together, they can be particularly helpful in treating long-standing local infections which are not resolving.

Apis/Levisticum

Homeopathic potencies of honey-bee poison (Apis mellifica) and lovage (Levisticum officinalis).

Useful in treating earache, particularly middle-ear infections, under the supervision of a doctor. Up to five pills every two to three hours. For babies, they can be dissolved first in a teaspoon of water.

Carbo Betulae comp. (POM)

Also known as Birkenkohle comp., it contains birch charcoal (Carbo betulae), an extract of camomile root (Matricaria chamomilla) and a homeopathic potency of antimony (stibium).

For diarrhoea. One capsule every two to three hours in acute cases, otherwise three times a day.

Disci comp. c. Argentum or Disci comp. c. Stanno (POM)

Mixture of homeopathically potentized substances including red-ant juice (formica) and bamboo nodes (Bambusa e nodo), with either argentum (silver) or stannum (tin).

Indicated for a variety of acute or chronic back and neck conditions, including sciatica and lumbago, and other neuralgic symptoms originating in the spine. Usually, a one millilitre ampoule is injected under the skin near the area where the symptoms originate. May be given daily or three times a week, depending on the severity of the condition. Unlike conventional painkillers, which tend to be the mainstay of conventional medicine in such conditions, they are aimed at speeding the natural healing process. Very often, if conventional painkillers are also needed, they can be quickly withdrawn as the symptoms resolve.

Ferrum Phos. comp. (POM)

Contains homeopathic potencies of monkshood (Aconitum napellus), white bryony (Bryonia alba), gum-tree leaves (eucalyptus), hemp agrimony (eupatorium), iron phosphate (ferrum phosphoricum) and sabadilla seeds (Schoenocaulon officinalis).

For colds and flu-like conditions, particularly in children. Five pills dissolved under the tongue every two to three hours at the first sign of a cold may be sufficient to prevent its further development.

For babies, two pills dissolved in a teaspoon of water should be given with the same frequency.

Gencydo (POM)
Contains an extract of lemon (Citrus medica) and quince (cydonia).

For hayfever and allergic rhinitis, a one-millilitre ampoule is injected two to three times a week. To prevent the onset of hayfever, it may be given in a three to six-week course in January or February. This can radically reduce the severity of any attack later in the year, and achieves a more long-lasting effect than just suppression of the symptoms.

Infludo (POM)
Same ingredients as Ferrum Phos. comp. except, instead of ferrum phosphoricum, a homeopathic potency of phosphorus is used, and it contains alcohol.

For influenza, flu-like illnesses and feverish colds. The inclusion of phosphorus and alcohol makes Infludo unsuitable for children (who should be given Ferrum Phos. comp.). Five to eight drops in a little lukewarm water every hour in the acute phase of the illness then, as it resolves, two to four times a day. This dose should be continued until recovery is complete to help prevent secondary infection and post-flu debility.

Iscador (POM)
A preparation of mistletoe (Viscum album) supplied in ampoules for injection. Two other preparations, Helixor and Viscum Abnoba, are also available (though not licensed in the UK).

For all forms of cancer and pre-cancerous conditions. Found to improve the patient's general physical and mental condition. Also contributes to pain relief and helps psychological adjustment to the illness *(see* Chapter 13).

Menodoron
Alcoholic extract of shepherd's purse (Capsella bursa-pastoris), sweet marjoram (Origanum majorana), yarrow (Achillea mille-folium), oak (Quercus cortex) and stinging nettle (Urtica dioica) in herbal preparations.

For a variety of menstrual problems, including irregular periods, the absence of periods (amenorrhoea), painful periods (dysmenorrhoea), heavy periods (menorrhagia) and premenstrual tension. It is the first line of treatment for all abnormalities of the menstrual cycle and is usually prescribed as ten to twenty drops, three times a day in a little water.

Silicea comp. (POM)
(See also entry in home remedies list.)

When treating acute or chronic sinusitis, injected ampoules tend to have a more powerful effect than the pills, and are used under the supervision of a doctor in severe cases.

15. The Medicines and Legislation

In the 1950s, the advent of many new synthetic drugs led to the development of a somewhat uncritical enthusiasm for using medicines. This was the time when a wide range of antibiotics was developed, steroids became available, and powerful sedatives and antidepressives appeared. It was not until the tragic side effects of the sedative, thalidomide emerged that a far more critical approach to the use of drugs began to prevail.[1] The public became more aware of the dangers of the new drugs through publicity of the deformities babies were born with after their mothers had taken thalidomide during the early stages of pregnancy.

Usually, when a new group of drugs is developed, a period of over-enthusiastic use is followed by a period when the side effects and dangers become apparent. It took very widespread use to reveal the full dangers of barbiturate addiction, and now their use is highly restricted. Similarly, it took two decades of widespread prescribing of benzodiazepines, such as Valium, before the medical profession realized that there was a danger of dependency. As general awareness of the dangers of using very powerful chemical drugs has increased, many people have become sceptical of conventional medical practice, and some have turned to complementary or alternative forms of medicine.

Within the medical profession as a whole, there has been little questioning of the fundamental direction of treatment. Instead, conventional medical solutions have been sought for the problems caused by conventional medical practice. After the thalidomide tragedy, the Committee for the Safety of Medicines was set up in the UK under Sir Derek Dunlop to address the dangers of medical prescribing. The committee's findings led to the Medicines Act of 1968, which established a licensing procedure for all medicines, under the authority of the Health Minister. It also set up the Medicines Commission to advise on the licensing criteria. One of the effects of this was to emphasize the importance of extensive animal testing of all new drugs before they went on the market; another was the development of a system whereby doctors reported side effects they noticed to a central authority. The aim was to reduce the time between serious side effects, including death, beginning to be recorded and the withdrawal of the relevant drug.

The exclusive experience of conventional drugs of the members of the Medicines Commission has given rise to the concept that all medicines have risks or dangers and that these have to be balanced against the benefits. As a result, not only does the licensing procedure demand evidence of the drug's safety, but also of its effectiveness and claimed benefit. The standardization and quality of manufacture is also examined, so the licensing authority evaluates three main aspects: safety, efficacy and quality. The whole system was designed in accordance with the conventional medical approach, with conventional drugs the focus of attention, although all medicines were to be required to hold licences. From the outset, little or no attention was paid to the quite different background to and characteristics of other medicines, such as herbal, homeopathic and anthroposophical medicines. All but one of the members of the Medicines Commission and the various specialist committees have been experts in conventional medicine and pharmacy. So it is hardly surprising that the regulations were attuned to conventional drugs, and are not necessarily appropriate for medicines used by any of the other approaches.

The greatest irony is that the so-called solution to the dangers of using conventional synthetic drugs endangers the availability of other types of medicines, which have never posed a significant safety problem. The Medicines Act and the Medicines Commission, as constituted at the time of writing, strengthen the monopoly of conventional practice in spite of the recognized dangers, while putting at risk the remedies used by other medical approaches which have been shown to be safer.

There have been various attempts by the conventional medical authorities to show that natural medicines, as they are often called, are also dangerous. They have been quick to point out that 'natural' does not necessarily mean safe, and rightly argue that some plants contain highly poisonous chemicals. The berries of deadly nightshade *(Atropa belladonna)*, for example, contain atropine and can be fatal if ingested in sufficient quantity. But what the conventional authorities have been slower to admit is that medical herbalists, who use plant-based medicines, have long been aware of the dangers of overdose and prescribe accordingly. In addition, the philosophy of medical herbalism is to use strong plant substances only when necessary. This contrasts with conventional medicine's propensity for using powerful drugs, many of which are derived from the same plant-based chemicals as the most powerful herbal medicines. For example, the powerful anti-spasmodic, atropine, is used in conventional practice while a gentler anti-spasmodic, camomile, has been neglected.

Although it cannot be claimed that none of the herbal and homeopathic medicines have ever produced side effects, those that have arisen have been much less serious than the problems experienced with conventional drugs. In homeopathy, it is acknowledged that after the initial treatment there may be a slight worsening of the symptoms, followed by an improvement. This is a characteristic of the way homeopathic medicines work. Some might see the slight worsening as a side effect, even though it is likely to be welcomed by the homeopathic doctor because it usually demonstrates that an improvement is to follow.

The recent study of the efficacy of anthroposophical medicines mentioned in Chapter 13 examined whether specific anthroposophical medicines had produced side effects. Some were reported for example, eczema could initially be aggravated when sulphur was given orally, and there could be pain and local reactions from low potency injections of remedies like apis, formica, Gencydo and Iscador. Also, it was reported that arnica ointment could provoke allergic skin reactions from patients who were allergic to the arnica plant. However, the side effects of some conventional drugs which remain licensed, such as aspirin (which can cause haemorrhaging in the gut), sedatives (which cause dependency), and steroids (which weaken bones) are far more serious.

The approach taken by the conventional medical authorities in the UK has been the basis for the removal of the licences of a number of herbal remedies and at least one homeopathic medicine. It might be imagined that herbal, homeopathic and anthroposophical medicines, which are so safe, would not have any difficulties with licences under a system set up to safeguard the public against dangerous medicines. However, when they appeal to the committees or to the Medicines Commission against the threatened loss of licences, they are confronted by the following kind of thinking.

From their experience of conventional drugs, the conventional medical experts who make up the committees naturally believe that any medicine which is efficacious must also have attendant dangers. They also believe the converse — that any medicine which is completely safe cannot have any beneficial effect. As the efficacy of the vast majority of anthroposophical and homeopathic medicines has not been demonstrated in clinical trials, and the members of the commission and the committees do not have any experience of prescribing them, they tend to consider them to be completely ineffective. The conventional medical experts see the licensing of medicines as a weighing of risks against benefits. So, if they start with the assumption that there is no benefit at all, by their own reasoning they must demand an infinite degree of safety. The slightest trace of a side effect would therefore make it difficult for them to recommend issuing a licence.

Such reasoning has led to ridiculous situations. The plant, Dutchman's pipe (aristolochia), contains aristolochic acid. If this chemical is fed to rats in enormous quantities, it causes them to develop cancer. Initially, the Medicines Division of the Department of Health proposed a ban on all homeopathic potencies of aristolochia, including the thirtieth decimal which contains less than one molecule of the substance per bottle. After an expensive appeal, fought by Weleda, a limit was introduced at the tenth decimal potency, allowing higher potencies to be used. The Professor of Toxicology supporting the manufacturer pointed out that this margin of safety demanded a level of carcinogens a million times lower than that accepted in bacon — in other words, this homeopathic medicine was required to be a million times safer than a plate of bacon and eggs before a licence would be issued.

Although the licensing system has the fully justifiable aim of safeguarding the public, in general, the basis for acquiring a licence goes beyond the question of safety to include quality and efficacy. As the medicines are assessed by weighing the benefits against the risks, there must be proof of their efficacy. This would seem reasonable enough, except that the required methods of proof load the dice very heavily against medicines from outside conventional practice. What is generally required is a testing method called a prospective double-blind randomized trial. It involves a large number of patients who are randomly treated with either the medicine or a placebo (dummy), without knowing which they are being given. For forty years, this has been the gold standard of conventional medicine and has been most practical with drugs expected to have powerful, easily identifiable effects. It is less practical in the assessment of gentler medicines which stimulate the body's healing response.

Conventional drug companies have had to use this method to test completely new substances. But there is considerable doubt within medical herbalism, homeopathy and anthroposophical medicine whether it could ever be appropriate for these medicines. One of the many difficulties is that the patient's constitution tends to be as much an indicator for use of a particular medicine as the symptoms of the illness. Even if it were possible to demonstrate the effects of these medicines with such methods, the cost of a single trial can easily reach half a million pounds. A multinational drug company marketing a handful of drugs may be able to absorb that level of cost but it is quite another prospect for a small business making some two thousand medicines.

Usually more than one trial indicating efficacy is demanded before doctors become convinced of the usefulness of a conventional drug, which has the advantage of being assessed by experts who are committed to the philosophy and practice of conventional medicine. The herbal, homeopathic and anthroposophical medicines are presented to the same experts, even though their background and training tends to bias them against medicines other than those used in conventional practice. The formal requirement for them to recommend the issuing of full licences to anthroposophical and homeopathic medicines is their acknowledgement that the medicines are effective. But such an acknowledgement would begin to integrate anthroposophical and homeopathic medicines into mainstream medicine. Making their licensing dependent on such an unlikely event put remedies other than conventional medicines in serious danger of becoming unavailable.

This was the case until the 1980s, when manufacturers and consumers of natural medicines became aware of the danger and two main campaigning organizations were set up. Manufacturers formed the Natural Medicines Group, and consumers the Natural Medicines Society. The fundamental problem was identified as the lack of experts from outside conventional medicine on the Medicines Commission and the various advisory committees. The framework of the Medicines Act provided powers for the Health Ministry to set up whatever sub-committees were considered necessary, operating under the Medicines Commission. The new groups campaigned for a Natural Medicines Committee, composed of experts from the four main schools (herbal, homeopathic, anthroposophical and biochemic).

Initially, the campaign appeared to fall on deaf ears. Health ministers and officials at the Medicines Control Agency expressed the view that experts in conventional practice were able to judge all forms of medicine so no special committee was needed. They also said all homeopathic and anthroposophical medicines on the market before 1968 were entitled to Product Licences of Right, and that as no date had been set for these provisional licences to be reviewed or terminated the medicines were in no immediate danger.

However, by the end of the 1980s, most herbal medicines had been reviewed and it had been decided that as long as they were sold only for the treatment of what was termed 'mild and self-limiting disorders,' double-blind clinical trials would not be required. Instead, 'bibliographic evidence' — references in authoritative books on herbalism or scientific journals supporting their use as remedies — was deemed to be sufficient. Traditionally, herbal products contain a large number of different herbs, and great pressure was put on manufacturers to use fewer ingredients. The composition of many medicines had to be changed before licences were granted, and the manufacturers were prevented from advertising various uses, such as treatment for arthritis or sleep-lessness. In the light of these difficulties, many manufacturers of herbal products did not even apply for licences. Those who did, applied for a limited number of medicines which they thought had reasonable chances of success. It has been estimated that, as a re-sult, fewer than twenty per cent of the herbal products on the market under provisional licences in the 1970s remained avail-able after the full licensing procedure.

The situation began to change for anthroposophical and home-opathic medicines with the preparation of a new European Commission directive on the regulation of homeopathic products. While making no specific provision for experts in anthroposoph-ical or homeopathic medicine to be involved in the licensing pro-cedure, it did provide for a simplified registration process. This exempted many homeopathic remedies from having to prove effi-cacy, as long as the manufacturer made no claims about the prod-uct's efficacy. Medicines given by injection were excluded, as were homeopathic products more concentrated than the fourth decimal potency.

Although anthroposophical medicine was included in early drafts of the directive, it was left out of the main body of the final version, receiving only a mention in the introduction. Estimates suggested that only about twenty per cent of anthroposophical remedies — many of which are either not potentized or contain substances more concentrated than the fourth decimal potency — were eligible for the simplified registration process. So this step forward for homeopathic medicines did little to improve the out-look for anthroposophical medicine.

However, the publication of the directive in 1992 prompted the Medicines Control Agency to reconsider the question of whether there should be a specialized committee representing homeopath-ic medicines. In 1994, The Advisory Board on the Registration of Homeopathic Medicinal Products was appointed. This was a big breakthrough for homeopathic medicines, although at the time no one was appointed to the board with specific expertise in anthro-posophical medicine. Three years later, however, new members were appointed, including an anthroposophical doctor who had been recommended by the Anthroposophical Medical Association.

This appointment was taken to signify that the Medicines Control Agency was at last serious about including anthroposophical medicines in the homeopathic registration procedure. Yet in spite of these steps forward, at the time of writing, eighty per cent of anthroposophical medicines still remain outside the simplified registration process. They are available on the market only through Product Licences of Right, which were always intended to be provisional, and their continued availability still needs to be safeguarded.

Another unresolved problem of the present regulatory system is that because so few herbal medicines are registered, many manufacturers now market herbal remedies as *nutritional supplements*. An example of the effect of this is that, despite empirical evidence of the value of hypericum (St John's Wort) as a herbal anti-depressant, it is not licensed as such. As it cannot therefore be advertised as suitable for depression, it is difficult for consumers to know that this treatment exists. Then, to obtain it, they must know that it can only be bought as a nutritional supplement.

In September 1999, a new EC regulation was issued, potentially making it possible for European Union countries to exempt all medicines that have been on the market for at least ten years from having to demonstrate efficacy and safety through double-blind clinical trials. Instead, bibliographic evidence would be sufficient. At the time of writing, it is too early to say exactly how this ruling will be applied in practice. If it proves to be possible to use it across the board with natural medicines, it would radically improve the legal status of the eighty per cent of anthroposophical medicines still in danger, as well as many herbal remedies currently being sold under the guise of nutritional supplements.

Continued vigilance and active campaigning remain essential to ensure that these potentially positive developments bear fruit. The Advisory Board on the Registration of Homeopathic Medicinal Products must have its remit widened to include efficacy issues if anthroposophical and homeopathic medicines are to be authorized on the basis of bibliographic evidence. Also, experts in herbal medicine must be involved in their licensing.

To deal with these issues at a European level, the Natural Medicines Society in the UK joined forces with similar societies in Germany, the Netherlands, France, Italy, Switzerland, Spain, Ireland, Denmark and Greece to form a body called the European Federation of Natural Medicines Users (EFNMU). This campaigned over the wording of the EC directive and has been involved in submissions on its remaining defects.

Natural medicines face different problems in different countries. Supporters of natural remedies in pre-unification West Germany forced a change in the law resulting in the plurality of medical approaches becoming legally recognized. Medical herbalism, homeopathy and anthroposophical medicine were each given their own medicines commission comprising experts nominated by the professional association of doctors in the respective fields. Each commission was granted the authority to set standards of safety and efficacy for its own medicines, thereby avoiding the problems associated with handing conventional medicine a state-supported monopoly. However, this positive step has recently been challenged as an infringement of the Treaty of Rome, as it goes beyond what is allowed for in existing EC directives.

In France, the position of anthroposophical medicines has been very difficult, in spite of the fact that the country is bound by EC directives. There, the majority of anthroposophical medicines can be prescribed only as 'magistral' preparations. This means the doctor has to list all the ingredients of a particular medicine and their quantities on the prescription, as if the pharmacist would be making up the remedy individually, even though a pre-prepared mixture is actually being supplied.

For example, instead of simply prescribing the anthroposophical medicine, Cardiodoron (also known as Onopordon Comp.), the doctor would have to list the three component plants and their concentrations. The problem is that this loophole, through which the medicines are allowed to be prescribed, could be closed at any time. Also, because the French authorities hold a register of permitted ingredients for medicines, any remedy which contains a single unregistered substance may not be prescribed at all.

In the United States, medicines must be approved by the Food and Drug Administration (FDA) before they can be marketed. This generally means that the manufacturer has to submit extensive evidence of the drug's efficacy, safety and quality to the authority. No anthroposophical or homeopathic medicines have been approved in this way and, until 1988, when the FDA issued a Compliance Policy Guide, their legal status was unclear. The guide laid down conditions governing the marketing of homeopathic medicines throughout the country. Shops are allowed to sell them over the counter if they are for minor ailments. Toxic substances in potentially harmful strengths and medicines for more serious complaints are restricted to prescription-only sale.

All homeopathic medicines are required to carry indications for use, unlike in Europe, where it has generally been a condition of exemption from conventional testing that no indications are given on the packaging. As homeopathic medicines can often be used to treat a variety of conditions, it can be very difficult for a manufacturer to decide on one or two ailments to print on the packaging. There simply is not room for a full list, and these limited indications can lead to a narrow view of the uses of the medicines.

The Homeopathic Pharmacopoeia of the United States is the main book of standards for homeopathic medicines. A medicinal substance has to meet the Pharmacopoeia's criteria for eligibility to be accepted as an official drug. The FDA's policy guide defines homeopathic remedies as those listed in the Pharmacopoeia, and also listings in reputable homeopathic *materia medica,* but does not refer specifically to anthroposophical medicines. However, as many of the potentized substances used in anthroposophical medicine are listed in the Pharmacopoeia, they are covered by the guide. The Pharmacopoeia also includes homeopathic medicines prepared as ampoules for injection and a number of methods of preparation which are typical of anthroposophical pharmacy, such as the use of specific temperatures. This means that the FDA's recognition of the Pharmacopoeia has made the majority of anthroposophical medicines legally available in the US. For those that are not listed, inclusion in the Pharmacopoeia requires the submission of a detailed monograph, along with extensive evidence of the medicine's therapeutic value. As there are more than a hundred substances used in anthroposophical medicine that are not yet listed, there is much work to be done before the full range of anthroposophical treatment will be available.

Many other countries take their cue for regulating medicines from what is happening in the US or Europe. For this reason, progress in these regions must be monitored with great care, as it is most likely to influence the availability of natural medicines worldwide.[2]

16. Therapeutic Communities

The practice of anthroposophical medicine embraces the environment in which patients are treated as much as the therapies and remedies that are used. It includes the way doctors, nurses and therapists work together, the way they are paid, and how the health care is itself financially supported. In anthroposophical medicine, it is considered that the way medical staff relate to each other and make decisions can profoundly affect the outcome of treatment.

This idea has also been explored within conventional psychiatry. In the 1940s and 1950s, two doctors, David Clark and Maxwell Jones, developed methods of group decision-making which broke from the usual hierarchical structure to involve all the staff, and even the patients, in the running of a hospital or ward. Their notion of a therapeutic community saw the administration of the psychiatric unit as something which could be either beneficial or damaging to the health of patients, depending on how it was done. They had noted that most of the administrative decisions were made by the consultant or chief nurse, and that the hierarchical atmosphere tended to force the rest of the staff and the patients to be passive, thereby blocking their initiative and creative input. The more democratic system they recommended is still operated in a number of psychiatric units, but has remained a minority approach within psychiatry as a whole.

In the treatment of physical illnesses within conventional medicine, there have been attempts to develop teamwork, with greater participation by nurses, physiotherapists and others in case conferences about specific patients. But these ideas have generally remained superficial in practice, with the doctor still very much in charge. And, even among the few psychiatric units orientated towards the therapeutic community idea, there have been no breaks from the usual hierarchical structure in the way the staff are paid.

During the Second World War, an anthroposophical doctor from Vienna, Karl Konig, established a therapeutic community for the care of mentally handicapped children at Camphill, near Aberdeen in Scotland. Working with a group of doctors and educators who were refugees from Austria, he set it up with common ownership of property where the workers were paid according to the needs dictated by their personal circumstances. They lived with the handicapped children, all together as extended families. The children received an education based on the normal curriculum and were treated with a wide range of therapies from anthroposophical medicines to therapeutic eurythmy.

At the time, there was very little provision for the mentally handicapped beyond hospitals for the subnormal, where there was almost no attempt at treatment or education. The attitude then was more akin to 'out of sight, out of mind' than the relatively enlightened attitudes which have prevailed since the 1960s, when conventional schools and training centres for handicapped people began to be established and they became more accepted in society. As the Camphill children grew up, village communities developed, such as Botton Village at Danby, in North Yorkshire, where workshops and farms gave them work and they were again integrated into the extended families of the staff. The emphasis was less on therapy and more on finding a lifestyle in which handicapped adults could be integrated into society while also contributing to it.

At the Camphill schools, a method was developed to help staff cope with children with particularly difficult problems. In the college meeting, as it was called, they built a complete picture of the child's history, constitution and the nature of the problem, with contributions from the doctor, other therapists, the teacher and those who lived with the child. The deeper understanding which resulted often gave rise to ideas of how to help the child. As a testimony to the therapeutic community approach, there are now many Camphill centres around the world, and this is probably the area of anthroposophical work which is best known to the general public.

It was through a group of people who had been involved with the Camphill movement that Park Attwood Clinic, near Kidderminster in England, was founded in 1979. Their aim was to found a centre where people suffering from physical illnesses or psychiatric problems would be supported in a setting which would feel like a real home, compared with the clinical atmosphere of most hospitals. The whole range of anthroposophical treatment was to be provided in a residential setting. At the time of writing, the clinic had fourteen beds, an outpatient department, three full-time doctors and a team of nurses. It also offered therapeutic massage, hydrotherapy, eurythmy therapy, and artistic therapies including painting and sculpture. Bringing all the therapies together enabled them to support each other and integrate into an intensive treatment programme. The college meeting idea was further developed into a system of regular case conferences where the doctors, nurses and therapists each described what they had observed about the patient, without immediately jumping to a conclusion about what they felt needed to be done.

Experience has shown that each profession brings a different perception of the patient to these meetings. The doctor brings the case history, aspects of the patient's biography and the results of physical examination. The therapeutic masseur describes the distribution of warmth in the patient's body, and a detailed picture of the states of tension in the muscular system and the tone of the bodily tissues. The therapeutic eurythmist brings an image of how the patient moves, and artistic therapists describe the patient's creative expression. Nurses add to this their view of the patient's physical and psychological condition, gained through 24-hour care. Out of this collection of observations, a motif usually emerges.

This motif often provides a qualitative extension to the conventional diagnosis, and paints a broader picture within which to understand the illness. It has a diagnostic significance and points to the common therapeutic direction which needs to be taken. This broad indication is worked out in detail by each professional, to arrive at the appropriate doctor's prescription, the type of nursing treatment required and the direction the artistic therapies should take. The therapeutic and creative initiatives of each member of the case conference can, in this way, be brought into play. It is a quite different process from when the conventional doctor makes the diagnosis alone, prescribes for the patient and gives instructions to the other therapists. It is also quite different from what would be the case if each therapist made an independent diagnosis and gave treatment in isolation.

Another social aspect which can affect those working together in an anthroposophical practice concerns the relationship between work and remuneration. Steiner suggested that the link between the two would have to be broken, or at least loosened, if people were to develop a sense of karma and of true freedom, which involves responsibility for their actions. For example, people in the army follow orders — that is what the job demands. Therefore, their actions are largely determined by others, and it could be said that they have handed over their freedom and responsibility to the commanders. Similarly, people who are paid to work are directed by their employers, and their freedom of action is limited by those people who are prepared to pay for their labour. The extent to which they are limited varies enormously, but this often leads to an attitude of 'I'm just doing my job' — particularly to excuse an action of dubious morality. In the practice of medicine, doctors and therapists work with the intimate details of patients' lives, and can directly affect their futures. This calls for a sensitivity to, and respect for, the patients' particular paths through life, and their freedom to make their own decisions. The doctors or therapists must take this into account when deciding on treatment, while also maintaining their own therapeutic freedom and sense of responsibility.

Some doctors and therapists have incorporated these principles into the way they work. For example, at Park Attwood Clinic staff remuneration has been related more to the needs arising from personal circumstances than to the particular work done, as in the Camphill case described above. This means that anyone with a large family to support has been likely to receive more than an unmarried person, regardless of their respective jobs. Many professional people find that their motivation comes more from the work itself than from the salary, and an arrangement like that at Park Attwood can intensify this feeling. It is a far more demanding way of working — for example, such a system tends to go hand-in-hand with a less rigid job description, and doing what needs to be done rather than just following instructions. It demands a wider awareness of different areas of work and a responsible attitude towards the needs of others, because the level of remuneration of any one person has economic consequences for the whole community. A stronger sense of community can result from working this way, and this is something patients often sense. Together with the influence of the intensive case conferences, this can contribute to a beneficial therapeutic effect.

Health care in the UK falls into two main categories: the National Health Service and private treatment. As the NHS provides free health care as of right, whereas private care is available only on payment of a set price, private care is treated more like a commodity within the economy. It seemed to those founding Park Attwood Clinic that the positive aspect of the NHS was that treatment was available to all, regardless of means. But a drawback was that it was state-controlled, and suffered from the suppression of staff initiative which was typical of such bureaucracies. It limited the choices available to patients, and encouraged them to lose their sense of responsibility for their own health. Patients also lost touch with the need to support the providers of health care, because a limitless amount appeared to be funded by taxation.

The positive aspect of the private system seemed to be the greater autonomy for the providers of health care and the freedom of choice and sense of responsibility engendered in patients. A major drawback, however, was that only patients with sufficient means could obtain care, and health tended to be treated as a commodity to be bought and sold. The founders of Park Attwood Clinic felt that health care should not be seen as a right or as a commodity. They considered that the best way to treat it was as a gift to patients with, ideally, the provision of such care supported in turn by contributions or gifts to the clinic.

The NHS allows its general practitioners considerable therapeutic freedom. In this context, anthroposophical medicine can be offered within a health service general practice, but it is not possible for independent groups of doctors to develop hospitals and have them incorporated into the NHS.[1] When Park Attwood Clinic was set up as a small hospital, the doctors wanted to offer their services to anyone, regardless of their means, along the lines of NHS hospitals. A charitable trust was established, to which people

who supported anthroposophical medicine could make regular donations. While undergoing treatment, patients were expected to
make contributions in accordance with their means, instead of a
fixed fee. It was hoped that they would become regular contribu-
tors to the trust after being discharged, if they had not been be-
forehand. As a registered nursing home, the clinic was also able to
receive payments from private health insurance companies.

In the early years, the flow of regular donations was sufficient
to meet about a third of the running costs of the clinic. Another
third was covered by patients' contributions during treatment, but
a third still had to be raised from charitable sources. As the clinic developed and expanded, the proportion of running costs covered by regular donations fell, and a greater proportion therefore
had to be met by patients undergoing treatment. More recently,
Park Attwood has set up a patient plan. Under this scheme, patients make regular payments to the clinic, irrespective of whether
they are receiving treatment. This guarantees them full care when
they need it, even if they cannot afford to pay at the time. Patients
not on the plan would generally be expected to meet the full cost
of any treatment when it is given, although each case is looked at
individually. Decisions regarding admissions are made on medical grounds and financial arrangements are agreed with the patient separately. The staff at Park Attwood are convinced that this
way of working can enhance the healing power of the medicines
and therapies, without distancing the clinic's work from mainstream health care provision.

Park Attwood has also received funding directly from health
authorities. A number of these, and also local groups of GPs who
control a common budget, have paid the full cost of admissions
from their areas. Some patients have also had their costs met by
private medical insurance. But in spite of all these various sources
of regular income, the clinic remains dependent on additional
fund-raising and occasional legacies and one-off donations. Some
patients have been so deeply moved by their experience of the
quality and intensity of care provided at Park Attwood, they have
made substantial donations and bequests to try to help this valuable work continue.

17. Extending Health Care Provision

In keeping with its aim to be an extension of conventional medicine rather than an alternative, anthroposophical medicine has largely developed within the main health care provisions of each of the countries where it has become established. It seeks to extend and bring innovation to the conventional health care systems by working within the system, not in opposition to it.

The first anthroposophical doctor to work as part of the National Health Service in the UK was Norbert Glas, whose practice in Gloucester joined the health service at its inception in the 1940s. His patients came from a very broad spectrum of society, and always included local people who had no particular interest in a different form of medicine but simply chose him as their GP. There were also some who were involved in the anthroposophical movement and many families whose children attended the local Rudolf Steiner School, Wynstones, near Gloucester. His successor developed the practice by including a therapeutic eurythmist, a therapeutic masseur and hydrotherapist, an artistic therapist and a counsellor. The main building for the practice and accommodation for the therapists was provided by St Luke's Trust, a charitable organization set up for the purpose. The additional therapies required financial contributions from patients, even though the expanded work developed closely alongside the NHS practice, from which patients were referred.

Through vigorous national and local fundraising, which involved many of the patients, and also further NHS funding, the trust has been able to build a new centre to house both the health service practice and a range of therapists. Regular meetings for patients take place at least monthly, and there are workshops in which patients, doctors and therapists share their experiences of a particular illness or problem. Comments focus on what has been found to be helpful, and from these meetings the beginnings of self-help groups are emerging. There are also regular feedback evenings. At the most recent of these, the main area of concern was to develop initiatives to overcome the social isolation felt by some patient groups. For example, the elderly, those suffering from long-term mental illness and parents struggling with young children.

The trust recently extended its old property, which now operates as a small residential community for adults with learning difficulties. It is run according to the Camphill principles described in the previous chapter. Various initiatives are being undertaken to help provide a social focus for certain groups of patients. For example, a weekly parent and toddler group is offering parenting support, while a gardening group is transforming two acres of grounds surrounding the new centre and the original building. A group of volunteers has set up a café, and a weekly craft session provides a meeting place for a number of people struggling with long-term health problems who might otherwise be socially isolated. Links are being developed with the Lansdown Pottery, the Hibernia School of Artistic Therapy, the Lindens Family Centre and the Painswick Inn Project for Homeless Young People, all in Stroud, Gloucestershire. It is felt that an enriched cultural and social life, which can benefit patients in many ways, is best achieved in partnership with existing local initiatives.

This kind of philosophy has much in common with the Healthy Living Centres currently being furthered by health ministers. These are lottery-funded schemes promoting health classes and social activities, often using medical centres as their focal point. One minister said the Healthy Living Centres should have 'a rounded vision which encompasses the psychological dimensions of health,' and that this meant 'working with local agencies to alleviate the problems which feed a mentality of despair' while building self-confidence, self-esteem and self-reliance as the 'bedrock of good health.'

A similar extension of a health service general practice has been developed in Bristol, where three part-time GPs work with a group of therapists at the Helios Medical Centre. One of the doctors there also runs a special clinic for children with learning difficulties, providing a range of anthroposophical medicines and therapies for their special needs. Another of the doctors, who has links with Bristol Cancer Centre, prescribes Iscador treatment and other anthroposophical therapies for cancer patients.

The Blackthorn Trust in Maidstone, Kent, was the first medical centre in the UK to be designed by anthroposophical architects. They were asked to produce a building and environment which, through the use of form and colour, would provide a therapeutic setting for the work of the doctors and therapists. The result was an inspiration for the new building at St Luke's in Stroud and the remodelling of an existing building at the Helios Centre.

The doctor who started the centre in Maidstone began by employing a part-time artistic therapist to work with patients who were not responding to other treatments. He noticed how successful this form of therapy was with these patients and expanded the range to include therapeutic eurythmy, and later music therapy. He also offered to treat difficult cases from other GPs who felt they could do no more.

When the Blackthorn Trust was set up to fund this treatment, it attracted considerable interest. It received a direct grant from the local health authority to pay for both treatment and a research project to assess its effectiveness. To supplement the therapies, groups were formed to help people with particular problems, such as anxiety or nervousness. Members worked on specific exercises and also benefited from the mutual support such a group can provide. A number of patients were so impressed by the help they received that they started doing craft work together and sold their wares to support the trust. This venture has brought a creative activity and the warmth of company to many lonely people, and a charity shop has opened which raises further funds for the trust's work.

The administrator for the health authority responsible for family practitioner services in the area described the work of the Blackthorn Trust as one of the most exciting developments in general practice. The authority has agreed to pay seventy per cent of the salaries of the therapists, with the remainder financed by the practice's income. This makes them as much a part of the NHS as practice nurses and receptionists, who have traditionally been financed in this way.

In further recognition of the trust's achievements, it was granted additional funds which it used to set up a café, bakery and small
garden centre. This was initially to provide a therapeutic work centre for long-term psychiatric patients but the Blackthorn Garden
Project now also receives referrals from other GPs, especially patients they are finding difficult to treat. The success of this project
inspired the development of other NHS practices working with anthroposophical medicine, including the Camphill medical practice
near Aberdeen, the Mytton Oak project in Shrewsbury and a second small practice in Maidstone at Park Wood.

These general practices, together with a residential medical
centre at Park Attwood, are being evaluated in a research project
for the Department of General Practice and Primary Care at St
Bartholomew's hospital in London and the Royal London School
of Medicine. The aim of the study is for the conventional medical
authorities to see whether valuable lessons may be learned from
the anthroposophical approach for the future development of general practice across the UK.

Extending general practices to include various therapists was
mainly pioneered in the Netherlands, where most cities have a practice operating along these lines. Typically, a group of doctors and
therapists converted a large house into what they called a 'therapeu-
ticum.' Patient groups were formed at these centres and given courses on how to look after their own physical and mental health. The
courses included such subjects as the value of wholefood nutrition,
an anthroposophical approach to childcare, meditative and other exercises, and lectures on anthroposophical medicine. Active patient
participation was encouraged and, together with the creativity which
the artistic therapies demanded, these courses contributed to coun-
terbalancing the rather passive role associated with taking medicines
and having physical treatments. These patient groups have also united to help defend the availability of natural medicines, which have
faced threats in the Netherlands as they have in the UK. More than a
hundred anthroposophical general practitioners work within the national health care system in the Netherlands.

When the School of Spiritual Science was founded at Dornach,
in Switzerland, in 1923, Dr Ita Wegman was appointed leader of
the Medical Section, which remains the focus of the worldwide

medical movement today. The Medical Section has special responsibility for medical training and research. Training seminars for medical students and doctors are run by the Medical Section at Dornach, with the main doctors' seminar held at the Lukas Klinik in neighbouring Arlesheim.[1]

Germany has a similar health care system to that of the Netherlands. Here, there are many hundreds of practising anthroposophical doctors and many thousands who prescribe some of the medicines. There are several specialist hospitals with between seventy and one hundred beds, including the Klinik Öschelbronn near Pforzheim, which is linked to the Carus Institut, one of the anthroposophical cancer research centres. All are integrated into the general health care system which, like the Dutch system, involves both state-subsidized and private insurance schemes. These fund patients in anthroposophical hospitals in the same way as in any conventional hospital. The Klinik Öschelbronn has introduced various innovative social measures, such as paying a proportion of the staff in accordance with their needs instead of the state rates, and administering the hospital through a clinic conference composed of any members of staff who wish to join. As well as these medical hospitals, there is also a psychiatric hospital with one hundred beds, the Friedrich Husemann Klinik, near Freiburg in the Black Forest.

A major development of anthroposophically inspired health care in Germany came about with the establishment of two large district general hospitals, one in the Ruhr — the Herdecke hospital — and one on the outskirts of Stuttgart — the Filderklinik. More recently, the community hospital at Havelhöhe, in Berlin, was taken over by an anthroposophical medical group with the aim of gradually converting it into an anthroposophically oriented general hospital. These provide the full range of specialities one would expect to find in any district general hospital, including accident and emergency, surgery, paediatrics, obstetrics and gynaecology, general medicine, and intensive care. All the methods of conventional medicine are available, but they are also extended through the use of anthroposophical medicines, physical treatments and artistic therapies. To set up and run hospitals on this scale, a new form of financial structure was developed.

In Germany, hospitals are usually run by the city or state authority, by religious organizations such as the Lutheran or Catholic Churches, or by charities such as the Red Cross. Others are private concerns, run in the same way as private companies. The anthroposophical hospitals were established as 'community hospitals for public benefit' — non-profit-making companies similar to charities. They are run by a circle of the leading doctors, nurses and administrators, and the doctors donate to the hospital any additional income earned from treating private patients. This money has been used to fund the therapists when their costs have not been recognized and supported by the health insurance schemes. It is also used to provide for training and research.

Herdecke hospital and the Filderklinik both offer state-recognized nursing training, teaching both conventional and anthroposophical skills, and at Herdecke, the larger of the two, an independent but fully recognized university offering medical training was established. While preparing students to sit the state medical exams, the university offers a relatively critical approach to conventional medicine, exposing students to its limitations as well as its strengths, and also gives the opportunity for students to be introduced to anthroposophical methods. Aspects of the teaching have also been influenced by anthroposophical ideas.

The Clinical Pharmacology Department at Herdecke University Hospital has published many academic papers and books on the problems of conventional methods of assessing drugs through clinical trials and tests on animals. The work, and the efforts of its main author, Gerhard Kienle, were major factors in forcing changes to Germany's Medicines Act, reversing the demand for such testing as the basis for the licensing of all medicines. Herdecke, which supports many of the specialist departments demanded by a university hospital, such as neurosurgery, was also one of the first hospitals in Germany to have its own department for computer-tomography (an advanced X-ray diagnosis technique). The hospital has aimed to stay at the forefront of conventional medical practice, while maintaining an awareness of its rightful role and complementing it with the full range of opportunities offered by anthroposophical practice.

The aim of anthroposophical medicine as a whole is to work with conventional medicine, while extending it through the insights gained from a spiritual knowledge of the human being. In practice, it works within conventional forms of health care provision, but introduces innovations based on these insights. The range of available anthroposophical health care extends from the small health service general practice to the district general hospital and university medical school. They serve as examples of what could develop into a future mainstream medicine.

Anthroposophical medicine has a substantial contribution to make to every aspect of health care. By so doing, it helps to counterbalance the predominantly materialistic and reductionistic view of the human being which is so fundamental to conventional medical practice. Anthroposophical medicine also helps to bring a balancing influence into society as a whole, which tends to be dominated by the same materialistic and reductionistic outlook.

Endnotes

Introduction

1. Natural science (or modern science), which nowadays is generally referred to as just 'science,' is here given its original name to avoid confusion with spiritual science.
2. Available under the title *Spiritual Science and Medicine* (Steiner Books).
3. *Fundamentals of Therapy, An Extension of the Art of Healing through Spiritual Knowledge* (Rudolf Steiner Press).
4. All these concepts are explained in detail in the following chapters.
5. For details of this process of development, *see* Steiner's books *Knowledge of the Higher Worlds, Occult Science* and *Theosophy* (all Rudolf Steiner Press).

Chapter 1

1. The etheric body, astral body and ego are also referred to as the life element, soul element and spirit respectively.
2. *Cellular Pathology as based upon Physiological and Pathological Histology,* a series of twenty lectures given in 1858.
3. All three non-physical aspects of the human — the life element, soul element and spirit — may be described as spiritual, but the spirit itself is the central core; the unique inner identity.

Chapter 2

1. In Chapters 13 and 14, practical steps in developing a medical treatment along these lines are described.
2. cf. D. W. Smithers, 'Cancer — an Attack on Cytologism,' *The Lancet*, 10 March 1962.
3. In his books, *Knowledge of the Higher Worlds* and *Occult Science,* Steiner describes how, with the help of certain exercises, the faculty of thinking can become an organ of perception in its own right.
4. It is clearly difficult to understand the spiritual realm without perceiving it directly, but the same difficulty is encountered by modern science in its investigations of the physical world. In nuclear physics, theoretical particles are studied which are so minute, they can only be 'perceived' at all by their apparent effects on other things. Similarly,

phenomena in space have been discovered which have only (so far) been explained by postulating the existence of 'black holes.' These again cannot be seen except in their apparent effects on other things. In the same way that the hypotheses of modern science can be used as working models, the results of spiritual science can also be understood and used, even without direct spiritual perception.

5. This polarity of physical forces, which centre on finite points, and etheric forces, which have a planar quality, is illustrated mathematically by projective geometry. George Adams, who did much original work in this field, used projective geometry to describe sets of laws for both realms (which he called space and counterspace) in his book *Physical and Ethereal Spaces* (Rudolf Steiner Press).

Chapter 3

1. It is acknowledged that plants also burn their own sugars and, particularly at night, give off carbon dioxide.

Chapter 4

1. This concept of reincarnation should not be confused with the teachings of certain ancient religions which suggest that humans can reincarnate as animals or insects. The human spirit is involved in the development of the human form as a vehicle through which it can act in the physical realm. Animals and insects do not have individual egos, and their bodily organizations are not developed to support them. The only bodily organization capable of supporting the human ego is the one the ego is itself active in forming.

2. The work of anthroposophical medical centres, including Park Attwood, is described in more detail in Chapters 16 and 17.

3. The fact that birds and mammals are warm-blooded does not imply that they have independent egos.

Chapter 6

1. The words homeopathy and allopathy are both derived from Greek, the prefixes homeo- meaning like and allo- unlike, while the suffix -pathy means suffering.

2. The example is largely based on the work of Margaret Colquhoun Ph.D. (cf. Science Forum, No. 8, Spring 1989, published by the Science Group of the Anthroposophical Society in Great Britain) and two botany workshops held at Park Attwood Clinic, England, in 1989 and 1990.

3. There is no suggestion here of following some kind of doctrine of signatures — an approach which has been rightly discredited. This doctrine is what remains of what may once have been a deeper art,

but which degenerated into the idea that plants which look like a particular human organ are good for treating that organ. The anthroposophical study of plants as remedies looks at the underlying formative processes, rather than particular physical features, in order to make connections with related processes at work in humans.

4. cf. *The Alchemical Studies* by C.G. Jung from his complete works.

Chapter 9
1. See Chapter 8.

Chapter 10
1. cf. 'Measles Virus Infection Without Rash in Childhood Is Related to Disease in Adult Life' by Tove Ronne, The Lancet, 5 January 1985.
2. *A Guide to Child Health* (see further reading list at back of book) is recommended for a detailed description of childhood illnesses. It should be noted that the examples of home remedies given are not alternatives to proper supervision by a doctor. *See* Chapter 14 for further details of dosages and methods of treatment.
3. Comp. is an abbreviation of compositum, and means a mixture. For example, Ferrum Phos. comp. contains a number of ingredients, the main one of which is ferrum phosphoricum.
4. Readers interested in finding out more about Rudolf Steiner education should contact their national anthroposophical society *(see* list at back of book).

Chapter 12
1. In anthroposophical medicine, certain metals are considered to be related to particular organs. For example, copper to the kidneys, tin to the liver, and silver to the reproductive organs. For details, *see The Metals,* L.F.C. Mees (Regency Press).
2. Her progress towards recovery was recorded in part of a BBC television series, *The Seven Ages of Man.*

Chapter 13
1. cf. 'Biologic Properties of Iscador: A Viscum Album Preparation' by Razvan Rentea, Edward Lyon and Robert Hunter, *Laboratory Investigation*, p 43, Vol 44, No 1, 1981.

Chapter 14
1. Further information may be obtained from the Biodynamic Agricultural Association, Painswick Inn Project, Gloucester Street, Stroud, Gloucestershire GL5 1QG.
2. The medicines in this list have been taken from the results of a re-

search project into the efficacy of anthroposophical medicines which
drew on the experiences of doctors in Britain. See 'On the Efficacy
of Anthroposophical Medicines' by Dr Michael Evans,
Complementury Medical Research, June 1991 Vol V, No 2, pp 71–78.

Chapter 15
1. Withdrawn in 1961.
2. Readers who wish to see natural medicines remain available may
   contact the Natural Medicines Society at PO Box 232, East Molesey,
   Surrey, KT8 1YF, England.This is also the address of the Secretariat
   of the European Federation of Natural Medicines Users.

Chapter 16
1. The NHS homeopathic hospitals all predate the health service and
   were taken over when it was set up.

Chapter 17
1. There is a list of courses around the world for doctors, nurses and
   therapists in Section 6 of Contact Addresses.

Further Reading

Introduction and Chapters 1-3
Occult Science, Rudolf Steiner, (Rudolf Steiner Press, London). An outline of spiritual science, or anthroposophy.

Rudolf Steiner: Scientist of the Invisible, A.P. Shepherd, (Floris Books, Edinburgh). An introduction to Steiner and his work.

Knowledge of the Higher Worlds, Rudolf Steiner, (Rudolf Steiner Press, London). Practical guidance on the inner strengthening required for the development of latent faculties of spiritual perception.

Physical and Ethereal Spaces, George Adams, (Rudolf Steiner Press, London). Describes a form of geometry which illustrates mathematically the laws of the physical and etheric realms.

The Metamorphosis of Plants, J.W. von Goethe, (Biodynamic Literature, Wyoming, RI). A collection of Goethe's writings on botany.

Fundamentals of Therapy, Rudolf Steiner and Ita Wegman, (Rudolf Steiner Press, London). A foundation work on anthroposophical medicine. (Requires a well-developed understanding of anthroposophy.)

Towards a Phenomenology of the Etheric World, J. Bockemühl (Ed.), (Rudolf Steiner Press, London). A collection of essays by scientists engaged in phenomenological research which introduces various aspects of the etheric world.

Chapter 4
Manifestations of Karma, Rudolf Steiner, (Rudolf Steiner Press, London). A description of the laws of karma and how, for example, events in one life can influence the bodily constitution and health in subsequent lives.

Chapters 5-6

Anthroposophical Medicine and its Remedies, Otto Wolff, (Published by
Weleda AG, Arlesheim, Switzerland and available from Weleda's national branches; *see* Section 3 of Contact Addresses). A booklet on
aspects of anthroposophical medicine. (Requires a well-developed
understanding of anthroposophy.)

The Science and Art of Healing, Ralph Twentyman, (Floris Books,
Edinburgh). Homeopathic and anthroposophical insights into the science and art of healing with a historical and mythological background.

Chapter 7

Fundamentals of Artistic Therapy, Margarethe Hauschka, (Rudolf
Steiner Press, London). A foundation work on artistic therapy, particularly painting therapy.

Chapter 8

Rhythmical Massage, Margarethe Hauschka, (Mercury Press, Spring
Valley, NY). Written as a textbook for those interested in training to
be therapeutic masseurs.

Chapter 9

Caring for the Sick at Home, Tieneke van Bentheim, Saskia Bos,
Ermengarde de la Houssaye, Wil Visser, (Floris Books, Edinburgh).
Describes basic nursing care, including details of herbal remedies
and how to administer them.

Chapter 10

A Guide to Child Health, Michaela Glöckler and Wolfgang Goebel,
(Floris Books, Edinburgh). A handbook for parents giving detailed
information on childhood ailments and the problems of child development.

Phases of Childhood, Bernard Lievegoed, (Floris Books, Edinburgh). A
detailed description of the physical and psychological development
which takes place during the seven-year phases of childhood.

Chapter 11

Phases: Crisis and Development in the Individual, Bernard Lievegoed,
(Rudolf Steiner Press, London). A Dutch psychiatrist writes about
the challenges of the different seven-year phases of life, from childhood to old age.

Man on the Threshold, Bernard Lievegoed, (Hawthorn Press, Stroud). A detailed account of the threshold of consciousness between the physical and spiritual worlds.

Chapter 12
Soulways, Rudolf Treichler, (Hawthorn Press, Stroud). A psychiatrist's insights into personal development and disorders of the soul. Includes addiction, neurosis, premature ageing, psychosis, anorexia, schizophrenia, depression and mania.

Rock Bottom: Beyond Drug Addiction, by members of Arta Rehabilitation Centre in the Netherlands, (Hawthorn Press, Stroud). Describes the work of the centre in treating and rehabilitating drug addicts.

Chapter 13
Aids, Arie Bos, (Hawthorn Press, Stroud), A practical approach to the understanding and treatment of Aids based on anthroposophical medicine.

Chapter 14
Biodynamic Agriculture: An Introduction, H.H. Kopf, B.D, Pettersson, W. Schaumann, (Rudolf Steiner Press, London). Detailed discussion of biodynamic farming and gardening, including explanation of the differences between organic, natural and biodynamic methods.

Chapter 15
Natural Medicines Society Newsletter. Published quarterly and available from the NMS, PO Box 232, East Molesey, Surrey, KT8 1YF.

The following articles may also be of interest to readers with respect to anthroposophical medicines and legislation:
'Controlled Clinical Trials and Medical Ethics' by R Burkhardt and G Kienle, *The Lancet* ,Vol. 2, 1978, pp 1356–59.
'Controlled Clinical Trials and Drug Regulations' by R Burkhardt and G Kienle, *Controlled Clinical Trials,* Vol. 1, 1980.

Chapter 16
Children in Need of Special Care, Thomas Weihs, (Souvenir Press, London). A description of the therapeutic community approach to the care of mentally handicapped children.

Focus. A biannual newsletter available from Park Attwood Clinic, Trimpley, Bewdley, Worcestershire DY12 1RE.

Chapter 17

Anthroposophical Medical Newsletter. Available from the Medical Group of the Anthroposophical Society in Great Britain, c/o Park Attwood Clinic, Trimpley, Bewdley, Worcestershire DY12 1RE.

Contact Addresses

1. Anthroposophical Societies

General Anthroposophical Society
Goetheanum
4143 Dornach 1 Switzerland
Tel. +41-61-706 4242
Fax +41-61-706 4314
Email: sekretariat@goetheanum.ch

Great Britain
*Anthroposophical Society in Great
Britain*
Rudolf Steiner House
35 Park Road
London NW1 6XT
Tel. +44-020-7723 4400
Fax +44-020-7724 4364
Email: rsh@cix.compulink.co.uk

Ireland
Anthroposophical Society in Ireland
3 Stewarts Place
Holywood, Co. Down BT18 9OX

United States of America
Anthroposophical Society in America
1923 Geddes Avenue
Ann Arbor MI 48104-1797
Tel. +1-734-662 9355
Fax +1-734-662 1727
Email:
information@anthroposophy.org

Anthroposophical Society in Hawaii
2514 Alaula Way
Honolulu HI 96822
Tel. +1-808-988 4555
Email: p-dwyer@aloha.net

Canada
*Anthroposophical Society in
Canada*
PO Box 38162
Toronto, Ont. M5N 3A8
Tel. +1-416-488 2886
Fax +1-416-488 5546
Email:
alexandragunther@anthroposophical.society.ca

Australia
*Anthroposophical Society in
Australia*
PO Box 5450
Kingston   ACT 2604
Tel. +61-2-6238 2116
Fax +61-2-6238 2701
Email:
anthroposophy.austra@bigpond.com

New Zealand
Anthroposophical Society in New Zealand
Beehive Gardens
Norton Road
4221 Hastings
Tel/Fax +64-6-876 7788
Email: hmulder@xtra.co.nz
www.anthroposophy.org.nz

South Africa
*Anthroposophical Society in
Southern Africa*
P.O. Box 71925
Bryanston 2021
Tel. +27-11-706 8545
Fax +27-11-706 8544

Up-to-date addresses can be found on
www.anthroposophy.net

Argentina
Sociedad Antroposófica en la Argentina
2224 Crisólogo Larralde
1429 Buenos Aires
Tel. +54-11-4702 9872
Fax +54-11-4710 3310

Austria
*Allgemeine Anthroposophische Gesell-
schaft Landesgesellschaft Österreich*
Tilgnerstrasse 3-5
1040 Vienna
Tel +43-1-505 3207
Tel/Fax +43-1-505 3454

Belgium
*Anthroposophische Vereniging in België
Société Anthroposophique en Belgique*
Oude Houtlei 2
9000 Gent
Tel. +32-9-233 5458
Fax +32-9-233 5327

Brazil
Sociedade Antroposófica no Brasil
Rua São Benedito 1325-c/45
04735-003 São Paulo
Tel. +55-11-523 0537
Fax +55-11-247 4552

Chile
Socieda Antroposófica de Santiago
Manuel Covarrubias 3782
Casilla 22-11 de Nunoa
Santiago de Chile
Tel. +56-2-223 0556

Columbia
Rama Santiago Apóstol, Cali
Uresa Bloque 54, apto. 203, Cali, Valle

Croatia
Antropozofsko Drustvo 'Marija Sofija'
Ulica Baruna Trenka br. 4
10000 Zagreb

Czech Republic (and Slovakia)
Anthroposofická Spolecnost
PO Box 285
11001 Prague 1
Tel. +420-2-651 7732

Denmark
Antroposofisk Selskab Danmark
Rosenvangsalle 251, 8270 Højbjerg
Tel. +45-8627 6060

Ecuador
Rama Micael, Quito
PO Box 17-04-10454, Quito
Tel. +593-2-407 621
Fax +593-2-449 032
Email: pjaramil@ramt.com

Egypt
Sekem Branch
PO Box 2834, Heliopolis, Cairo
Tel. +20-2-280 7994 / 7438
Fax +20-2-280 6959

Estonia
Eesti Antroposofiline Selts
Sireli 5/a, 0009 Tallinn
Tel. +372-2-518 035

Finland
Suomen Antroposofinen Liittoo
Uudenmaankatu 25 A 4
00120 Helsinki 12
Tel. +358-9-642 515
Fax +358-9-680 2591

France
Société Anthroposophique en France
2 rue de la Grande Chaumière
75006 Paris
Tel. +33-1-4326 0994
Fax +33-1-4325 2621

Georgia
Anthroposophical Society in Georgia
Chavtshavadse Avenue 19a
PO Box 32, 380079 Tbilisi
Tel. +995-32-352 739

Germany
Anthroposophische Gesellschaft in Deutschland
Rudolf Steiner-Haus
Zur Uhlandshöhe 10, 70188 Stuttgart
Tel. +49-711-164 3121
Fax +49-711-164 3130

Hungary
Anthroposophical Society in Hungary
Berènyi u.8,. 1016 Budapest

Iceland
Antroposofiska Felagid a Islandi
PO Box 953, 121 Reykjavik
Tel. +354-486 6022

India
5 Proctor Road, Grant Road
Mumbai (Bombay) 400 007
Tel/Fax +91-22-386 3799

Italy
Società Antroposofica in Italia
Via Privata Vasto 4, 20121 Milan
Tel/Fax +39-02-659 5558

Japan
Anthroposophical Society in Japan
Rudolf Steiner House Japan
Kikui-cho 20, Shinjuku-ku
Tokyo 162-0044

Latvia
Anthroposophical Society in Latvia
Uldis Saveljevs
Keldisa Str. 24-51, 1021 Riga
Tel. +371-2-171 282

Mexico
Rama Juan de la Cruz
Tecla 46, Col. Los Reyes
Coyoacan Mexico DF 04330
Tel. +52-5-617 6854
Fax +52-5-617 4054

Namibia
Anthroposophical Group in Namibia
PO Box 11359, 9000 Windhoek
Tel. +265-61-220 033

Netherlands
Anthroposofische Vereniging in Nederland
Boslaan 15, 3701 CH Zeist
Tel. +31-30-691 8316
Fax +31-30-691 4064

Norway
Antroposofisk Selskap i Norge
Prof. Dahlsgate 30, 0260 Oslo
Tel. +47-22-448 688
Fax +47-55-102 235

Peru
Sociedad Antroposófica en el Perú
Avenida Prescott 590, Lima, San Isidro
Email: hidrosa@ibm.net

Philippines
Anthroposophical Group in the Philippines
110 Scout Rallos Street
1103 Quezon City, Metro Manila
Tel. +63-2-928 3986
Tel/Fax +63-2-928 7608
Email: asp@info.com.ph

Poland
Towarzystwo Antropozoficzne w Polsce
ul. Sakowicza 6, 10-900 Olsztyn
Tel/Fax +48-89-523 7771

Portugal
Sociedade Antroposófica em Portugal
Rua D. Estefania N°. 99, 2° Drt
1000 Lisbon
Fax +351-1-354 0107

Romania
Societatea Antroposofica din Romania
Str. Matei Voevod 31, Sect. 2
73222 Bucharest
Tel/Fax +40-1-210 3357

188 ANTHROPOSOPHICAL SOCIETIES

Russia
Anthroposophical Society in Russia
Nastshokinski 6, kw. 3, 121019 Moscow
Tel/Fax +7-095-291 2384

Slovakia (see Czech Republic)

Spain
Sociedad Antroposófica de Espana
Calle Guipuzcoa 11-1-Izda
28020 Madrid
Tel. +34-1-534 8163

Sweden
Antroposofiska Sällskapet i Sverige
P1 1800, 153 91 Järna
Tel. +46-8-5515 0530
Fax +46-8-5515 0644

Switzerland
Anthroposophische Gesellschaft in der Schweiz
Hauptstrasse 12, 4143 Dornach
Tel. +41-61-701 5785
Fax +41-61-701 5717

Uruguay
Novalis Group, Montevideo
Amazonas 1529
11400 Montevideo
Tel. +598-2-619 3370

2. Anthroposophical Hospitals, Clinics and General Practitioners

Great Britain
Park Attwood Clinic
Trimpley, Bewdley. DY12 1RE
Tel. +44-1299-861 444
Fax +44-1299-861 375

Raphael Medical Centre
Rehabilitation and Nursing Home
Hollanden Park Coldharbour Lane
Hildenborough
Tonbridge TN11 9LE

Some General Practioners:
A current list can be found on
www.weleda.co.uk/antdoc.htm

Mytton Oak Foundation
Racecourse Lane,
Shrewsbury SY3 5LZ
Tel. 01743-357 350

Helios Medical Centre
17 Stoke Hill, Bristol BS9 1JN
Tel. 0117-962 6060

St Lukes Medical & Therapy Centre
53 Cainscross Road,
Stroud GL5 4EX
Tel. 01453-763 755

Camphill Medical Practice
St John's, Murtle Estate,
Bieldside, Aberdeen AB1 9EP
Tel. 01224-868 935
Fax 01224-868 971

North London Medical Practice
668 Finchley Road,
London NW11 7NP
Tel. 020-8935 1331

Anthroposophical Medical Practice
26 Hartfield Road,
Forest Row RH18 5DZ
Tel. 01342-824 422

Blackthorn Medical Centre
St Andrews Road,
Maidstone ME16 9AN
Tel. 01622-726 277

United States
Chrysalis Therapeutic Centre
Arlington, MA
Tel. +1-781-643-1449

*Community Supported
Anthroposophical Medicine*
Ann Arbor, MI
Tel. +1-734-677-7990

Fellowship Community
Spring Valley, NY
Tel. +1-914-356-8494

Hawthorn Clinic
Ghent, NY
Tel. +1-518-672-7004

K. David Schulz, PhD, ABPP
Woodbury, CT
Tel. +1-203-263-0290

Lawrence A. Fox, PhD
Baltimore, MD
Tel. +1-410-435-5420

Quantum Therapeutics
Silver Spring, MD
Tel. +1-301-989-1124

Raphael Association
Fair Oaks, CA
Tel. +1-916-967-8250

Steiner Holistic Medicine, Inc
Denver CO
Tel. +1-303-321-2100

Steiner Medical & Therapeutic Center
Phoenixville, PA
Tel. +1-610-933-1688

Canada
Kenneth McAlister, MD
Thornhill, Ont.
Tel. +1-905-882-4949

Werner Fabian, MD
Barrie, Ont.
Tel. +1-705-739-4114

Australia
Paulo Moraes MD
221 Wonga Road
Warranwood Vic 3134
Tel. +61-3-9876 3011
Fax +61-3-9876 4336
Email: moraes.arara@bigpond.com

New Zealand
Novalis House
275 Fifield Terrace
Christchurch 2
Tel/Fax +64-3-332 5702

Argentina
Therapeutikum San Rafael
Consultorios Médicos
Ramallo 2606, 1425 Buenos Aires
Tel. +54-11-4702 9888

Austria
Diät und Kneipp Sanatorium
6793 Gaschum / Montafon
Tel. +43-558-861 70
Fax +43-558-861 741

Brazil
Clinica Tobias
Rua Regina Badra 576
04641 São Paulo
Tel. +55-11-247 3799

Clinica Vivenda Sant'Anna
Rua Hermann Toledo 407
Bairro Sant'Anna
36037-210 Juiz de Fora MG
Tel. +55-32-231 1032
Fax +55-32-212 2776

Egypt
Sekem Medical Centre
El Katiba, PO Box 56
Belbes, Sharkia
Tel. +20-10-214 019

Estonia
Jakobs Therapeutikum
Jakobi 37, 51006 Tartu
Tel. +372-7-421 393
Fax +372-7-421 471

Germany
Filderklinik
Im Haberschlai, 70794 Filderstadt
Tel. +49-711-7703 0
Fax +49-711-7703 3679

Friedrich Husemann Klinik
Psychiatric and Neurological Clinic
79256 Buchenbach
Tel. +49-7661-382 0
Fax +49-7661-392 400

GFH Havelhöhe
Kladower Damm 221, 14089 Berlin
Tel. +49-30-36 501 0
Fax +49-30-36 501 444

Klinik Öschelbronn
Am Eichhof, 75223 Niefern-Öschelbronn
Tel. +49-7233-68 0
Fax +49-7233-68 110

Knapps-Krankenhaus Essen-Steele
Am Deimelsberg 34a, 45276 Essen
Tel. +49-201-805 4601
Fax +49-201-805 4603

Krankenhaus Lahnhöhe
Am Kurpak 1, 56112 Lahnstein
Tel. +49-2621-915 0
Fax +49-2621-915 575

Krankenhaus Rissen
Suurheid 20, 22559 Hamburg
Tel. +49-40-81910
Fax +49-40-813 019

Kreiskrankenhaus Heidenheim
Schlosshausstrasse 100
89522 Heidenheim
Tel. +49-7321-332 502
Fax +49-7321-332 048

Heilstätte Sieben Zwerge,
Drogenkrankheiten
Grünwangerstrasse 4
Postfach 1153, 88682 Salem
Tel. +49-7544-507 0
Fax +49-7544-507 51

Paracelsus-Krankenhaus
Burghaldenweg 60
75378 Bad Liebenzell
Tel. +49-7052-925 0
Fax +49-7052-925 215

Therapeutische Gemeinschaft für
Kinder- und Jugendpsychiatrie
Sonderkrankenhaus
79691 Neuen
Tel. +49-7673-7891

Italy
Casa di Salute Rafael
Palace Hotel, 38050 Roncegno

Netherlands
Bernhard Lievegoed Klinik
Prof. Brockhorstlaan
3723 MB Bilthoven
Tel. +31-30-225 5555
Fax +31-30-228 3096

Rudolf Steiner Verpleeghuis
Nieuwe Parklaan 58
2597 LD Den Haag
Tel. +31-70-306 8306
Fax +31-70-352 1262

Centre for the rehabilitation of addicts
Arta
Krakelingweg 25. 3703 HP Zeist

Romania
Central de Medicina Integrale
Nr. 146 cod 1985 jud. Timis
Masloc
Tel/Fax +40-47-562 915

Spain
Centro de Terapia Antroposófica
Calle Salinas 12,
35571 Puerto del Carmen, Lanzarote
Tel. +34-28-512 842
Fax +34-28-512 844

Sweden
Vidarkliniken
153 91 Järna
Tel. +46-8551-50510
Fax +46-8551-50171

Switzerland
Bezirksspital Langnau: Komplementär-
medizinische Abteilung
3550 Langnau i.E.
Tel. +41-34-409 2222
Fax +41-34-409 2323

Casa di Cura Andrea Cristoforo
Via Collinetta 25, 6612 Ascona
Tel. +41-91-791 1841

Ita Wegman Klinik
Pfeffingerweg 1, 4144 Arlesheim
Tel. +41-61-706 7171
Fax +41-61-706 7173

Lukas Klinik (for cancer)
Postfach 532, 4144 Arlesheim
Tel. +41-61-701 3333
Fax +41-61-701 8217

Merian Iselin-Spital
Dr. Med, Markus Greub
Föhrenstrasse 2, 4009 Basel
Tel. +49-61-305 1212
Fax +49-61-301 1866

Paracelsus-Spital
Bergstrasse 16, 8805 Richterswil
Tel. +41-1-787 2121
Fax +41-1-787 2351

3. Manufacturers and Distributors of Anthroposophical Medicines

Great Britain
Weleda (UK) Ltd
Heanor Road
Ilkeston
DE7 8DR
Tel. +44-115-944 8222
Fax +44-115-944 8210
Email: Info@Weleda.co.uk
www.weleda.co.uk

Ireland
Weleda (Irl.) Ltd
Scoughan,
Blessington
Co. Wicklow
Tel. +353-45-865 575
Fax +353-45-865 827

United States of America
Weleda Inc,
PO Box 249
Congers
NY 10920
Tel. +1-914-268 8572
Fax +1-914-268 8574
Email: Info@Weleda.com

Canada
Purity Life Health Products Ltd
6 Commerce Street
Acton, Ont. L71 2X3
Tel. +1-519-853 3511
Fax +1-519-853 4660

Australia
Weleda Pty Ltd
488 Burke Street
Melbourne
VIC 3000
Tel. +61-3-9723 7278

New Zealand
*Weleda New Zealand Lt*d
PO Box 8132
Havelock North
Tel. +64-6-877 7394
Fax +64-6-877 4989
Email:
customerservices@weleda.co.nz

South Africa
Weleda SA
PO Box 5502
Johannesburg 2000
Tel. +27-11-444 6921
Fax +27-11-444 8774
Email: eleanor@Pharma.co.za

Argentina
Weleda SA
Ramos Mejia 2615. 1609 Boulogne
Tel. +54-11-4737 0303
Fax +54-11-4737 0859
Email: gerencia@weleda.com.ar

Austria
Weleda GmbH & Co. KG
Hosnedlgasse 27, 1220 Vienna
Tel. +43-1-256 6060
Fax +43-1-259 4204
Email: Weleda@netway.at

Belgium
Weleda NV
Ambachtenlaan 8, 3001 Leuven
Tel. +32-16-406 624
Fax, +32-16-400 184
Email: WeledaBelg@compuserve.com

Brazil
Weleda do Brasil Ltda
Rua Brigadeiro Henrique Fontanelle 33
05125-000 São Paulo SP
Tel/Fax +55-11-3641 4122
Email: Weleda@Weleda.com.br

Chile
Weleda Chile Ltda
Simón Bolivar 4188, Nunoa, Santiago
Tel. +56-2-225 8953
Fax +56-2-225 3508

Czech Republic
Weleda spol.sro
Opatovicka 24, 110 00 Prague 1
Tel. +420-2-2491 5301
Fax +420-2-2491 6081
Email: Weledapraha@mbox.vol.cz

Denmark
A/S Todin
Postboks 216, 6200 Åbenrå
Tel. +45-7462 4488
Fax +45-7462 0966

Finland
Suomen Luonnonlaake Oy
Kyläsaarenkatu 14, 00580 Helsinki
Tel. +358-9-4114 7702
Fax +358-9-698 8214
info@weleda.fi

France
Weleda SA
9 rue Eugene Jung, 68330 Huningue
Tel. +33-3-8969 6800
Fax +33-3-8969 6899
Email: Weleda@hr.net.fr

Germany
Weleda AG
Postfach 1320,
73503 Schwäbisch Gmünd
Tel. +49-7171-919 414
Fax +49-7171-919 424
Email: info@weleda.de

Abnoba Heilmittel GmbH
Güterstrasse 53, 75177 Pforzheim

Helixor Heilmittel GmbH
Postfach 8, 72348 Rosenfeld

WALA-Heilmittel GmbH
73085 Eckwälden/Bad Boll

Hong Kong
Yung Trading Ltd
Flat 906, Block 20, Heng Fa Chuen
Tel. +852-9430 3384
Fax +852-2505 9566

Hungary
*GTT Hyppokrates Kereskedelmi es
Szolgaltato Beteti Tarsaag
Buro Weleda*, Paulay Ede u. 52,
Bocskai U 27, 1061 Budapest
Tel. +36-1-340 2379
Fax +36-1-340 2379

Iceland
Thumalina
Posthusstraeti 13, 101 Reykjavik
Tel. +354-551 2136
Email: Mar-@isholf.is

Italy
Amos srl
Via Pessano 11, 20151 Milan
Tel. +39-02-4009 0132
Fax +39-02-4007 0379
Email: amos-vicentini@iol.it

Japan
Nature's Way Co. Ltd
1-2-23 Nishiki Naka-ku,
Nagoya 460-0003
Tel. +81-52-232 1161
Fax +81-52-232 1162
Email: ichikawa@naturesway.co.jp

Netherlands
Weleda Nederland BV
Postbus 733, 2700 AS Zoetermeer
Tel. +31-79-363 1313
Fax +31-79-363 1303

Poland
PZA SA Multi Pharme
ul. Novogrodzka 200, 18-400 Lomza
Tel. +48-86-167 481
Fax +48-86-167 4826

Portugal
Farmacia Nova
Rua Bernardium Ribeiro 1A
2780 Caxias, Oeiras
Tel. +351-21-44 32837
Fax +351-21-44 32839

Russia
Weleda Russia
Zverinetskaya 34-38, 105318 Moscow
Tel. +7-095-369 2301
Email: Weledarus@Glas.apc.org

Spain
Weleda SA
Calle Manuel Tovar 3, 28034 Madrid
Tel. +34-1-358 0358
Fax +34-1-358 1247
Email: Weleda.spain@mad.servicom.es

Sweden
Weleda SB
Box 4, 153 21 Järna
Tel. +46-8-5515 1800
Fax +46-8-5515 1815
www.weleda.se

Switzerland
Weleda AG
Stollenrain 11, 4144 Arlesheim
Tel. +41-61-705 2121
Fax +41-61-705 2310

Taiwan
Sun-me Joint Enterprise Co Ltd
3F, 341 Tun-Hwa N. Road, Taipei
Tel. +886-2-2378 6339
Fax +886-2-2378 6018

4. Professional Associations of Anthroposophical Doctors

United Kingdom
*Anthroposophical Medical
Association*
c/o Park Attwood Clinic
Trimpley, Bewdley DY12 1RE
Tel. +44-1299-861 444
Fax +44-1299-861 375

United States of America
*Physicians' Association for Anthro-
posophical Medicine (PAAM)*
1923 Geddes Avenue
Ann Arbor MI 48104-1797
Tel. +1-734-930 9462
Fax +1-734-662 1727

Canada
*Canadian Anthroposophical
Medical Association*
Dr Kenneth McAlister
9100 Bathurst, Suite #2
Thornhill, Ont. L4J 8C7
Tel. +1-905-882 4949
Fax +1-905-882 0560

Australia
*Australian Anthroposophical
Medical Association Inc.*
Dr. Antony Underwood
802-808 Pacific Highway, Suite 2/2
Gorwon NSW 2072
Tel. +61-2-9418 1388
Fax +61-2-9418 1418

New Zealand
*New Zealand Association of
Anthroposophical Doctors*
Dr Roger Leitch
11 Woodford Road
Mount Eden, Auckland
Tel. +64-9-631 0477
Fax +64-9-843 3090

South Africa
*Anthroposophical Medical
Association, South Africa*
Dr. Raoul Goldberg
PO Box 760-
Howard Place 7450
Tel/Fax +27-21-531 5766

Argentina
*Asociación Argentina de Medicina
Antroposófica*
2224 Crisólogo Larralde
1429 Buenos Aires
Tel. +54-11-702 9872
Fax +54-11-502 5164

Austria
*Gesellschaft Anthroposophischer Ärzte
Österreichs*
Tilgnerstrasse 3, 1040 Vienna
Tel. +43-1-504 4908
Fax +43-1-504 8404

Belgium
Belgische Vereniging von
Antroposofische Aertsen
Sint Denijslaan 82, 9000 Gent
Tel. +32-9-221 6652
Fax +32-9-221 7710
Email:
Marnix.Schaubroeck@village.uunet.be

Brazil
Sociedade Brasileira de Médicos
Antroposoficos
Rua Regina Badra 576
Alta de Boa Vista
04641-000 São Paolo
Tel/Fax +55-11-247 3131

Bulgaria
Dr Kalina Atanasova Kostova
Sveta Troitsa, Block 376,
BX. D, App.101, 1309 Sofia
Tel. +359-2-201 028

Czech Republic
The Society of Anthroposophical Doctors
Dr Thomas Bouzek
Rooseveltova 31, 16000 Prague
Fax +420-2-2431 6525

Denmark
Dansk Selskab for Antroposofisk Medicin
Inge Alsted Pedersen
Maglegards Alle 110 st, 2860 Søborg
Tel. +45-3167 1159

Estonia
Society of Anthroposophical Doctors
Jaamamoise 1, 51006 Tartu
Tel/Fax +372-7-406 382

Finland
Antroposofisen lääketieteen lääkäriyhdistys
c/o Reijo Kurppa
Muuralankumpu 1 D 1, 02770 Espoo
Tel. +358-9-587 0408
Fax +358-9-859 4108
Email: pjzim@sci.fi

France
Le Mercure Federal
Olivia Curtis
12 rue Montaigne, 37300 Joue-les-Tours
Tel/Fax +33-2-4767 6642

Germany
Gesellschaft Anthroposophischer Ärzte
in Deutschland
Roggenstrasse 82, 70794 Filderstadt
Tel. +49-711-779 9711
Fax +49-711-779 9712

Italy
Gruppo Medico Antroposofico Italiano
Via Privato Vasto 4, 20121 Milan
Tel. +39-02 659 5558
Fax +39-02 6671 1563

Lithuania
The Society of Anthroposophical
Doctors
Dr. Ija Cimdina
Matisa 19-15, 1001 Riga
Tel. +371-7-229 8730
Fax +371-7-311 1939
Email: ijablum@hotmail.com

Netherlands
Nederlandse Vereniging van
Anthroposofische Artsen
Postbus 266, 3970 AG Driebergen
Tel. +31-343-533 538
Fax +31-343-533 651

Norway
Norske Legers Forening for
Antroposofisk Medisin
Dr. Arne Schjönsby, 2850 Lena
Tel/Fax +47-6116 0710

Peru
Asociacion Peruana de Medicina
Antroposofica
Frasiscco de Zela 2672, Lima 14
Tel/Fax +51-1-442 0528
Email: yvanille@blockbuster.com.pe

Poland
Towarzystwo Lekarzy
Antroposoficznych Polsce
Ewa Wasniewska
ul. Swietojanska 130-9, 81-401 Gdynia
Tel. +48-58-620 2775
Fax +48-58-620 1650

Russia
The Society of Anthroposophical Doctors
Prospekt Andropova 22-30
115533 Moscow
Tel/Fax +7-095-118 3001

Spain
*Asociacion de Médicos para
la Medicina Antroposófica*
Calle Guipuzcoa 11, 1-Izda, 28020
Madrid
Tel. +34-1-630 4448
Fax +34-27-418 447

Sweden
*LAOM (Läkarföreningen för
Antropofskt Orientered Medicin)*
Box 78, 15 300 Järna
Tel/Fax +46-8-5517 1883
Email: laom@post.netlink.se

Switzerland
*Vereinigung anthroposophisch orien-
tierter Ärzte in der Schweiz*
Dr. Med. Eva Streit, Paracelsus-Spital
Bergstrasse 16, 8805 Richterswil
Tel/ +41-1-787 2121 / 2750
Fax +41-1-787 2940

**European Federation of Natural
Medicine Users (EFNMU)**
President: Peter Meister
Beckweg 18, 58313 Herdecke,
Germany
Tel. +49-2330-623 328
Fax +49-2330-623 330
Secretary: Penny Viner
65 Church Street, Langham,
Oakham LE15 7JE, England

5. Support Groups

Great Britain
Medical Group of the Anthropo-
sophical Society in Great Britain
Park Attwood Clinic
Trimpley, Bewdley, DY12 1RE
Tel. +44-1299-861 444
Fax +44-1299-861 375

United States of America
The Federation of Natural Medicine
Users of North America (FONMUNA)
Christine Murphy
228 Hungry Hollow Road
Spring Valley NY 10977
Tel. +1-914 352 1967
Fax +1-914 426 5122

Austria
Verein für anthroposophisch
erweitertes Heilwesen
Schillerstrasse 6, 8010 Graz
Tel. +43-316-3210 7210
Fax +43-316-3210 7212

Belgium
Vereniging voor Antroposofische
Gesondheidszorg
Vredestraat 120, 2600 Berchem
Tel. +32-32-300 265

Finland
Antroposofisen lääketieteen yhdistys
(ALY)
Jaana Rahijärvi, PL 57, 00600 Helsinki
Tel. +358-9 757 3366
www.sci.fi/~pjzim/aly.htm

France
Association des Patients pour la
Defense de la Medicine d'Orientation
Anthoposophique
La Commanderie, 10140 Amance

Germany
Verein für ein erweitertes Heilwesen
Joh. Kepler Strasse 56/58, 75378 Bad
Liebenzell

Netherlands
Centrum Sociale Gesondheidszorg
Thedingsweert 3,
4012 NR Kerk Avezaath Tiel
Tel. +31-344-634 171

Poland
Oaraceksys-Terapeutikum
Przedsiebiorstwo Uslugowo,
ul. Slawkoska 10, 31-014 Kraków
Tel/Fax +48-12-227 206

Spain
Centro de Terapia Antroposófica
Calle Salinas 12, 35510 Puerto del
Carmen
Tel. +34-28-512 842
Fax +34-28-512 844

Sweden
Föreningen för Social Hygien
Jörgen Jannes
Marknadsvägen 207 2TR, 18 334 Täby

Switzerland
Verein für ein anthroposophisch erweit-
ertes Heilwesen
Postfach 5, 4144 Arlesheim
Tel. +41-61-701 1514
Fax +41-61-701 1503

6. Training Courses in Anthroposophical Medical Practice

Great Britain

Courses for doctors and medical students:
Anthroposophical Medical Association
Park Attwood Clinic
Trimpley, Bewdley DY12 1RE

Courses for nurses:
Anthroposophical Nurses Association
Julian Gilde
18 Alexandra Grove, London N4 2LF

Eurythmy therapy:
Peredur Centre for the Arts
Dunnings Road, East Grinstead
RH19 4NH

Artistic therapy:
Hibernia School of Artistic Therapy
Centre for Science and Art
Lansdown, Stroud GL5 1BB

Tobias School of Art
Coombe Hill Road, East Grinstead
RH19 4LZ

Speech therapy:
London School of Speech Formation
Dunnings Road, East Grinstead
RH19 4NH

United States of America

Courses for doctors, nurses, therapists:
Physicians' Association for
Anthroposophical Medicine
PO Box 269, Kimberton PA 109442

Brazil
Thirty-week course for doctors and nurses, also artistic therapy training:
Centro Paulus de Estudos
Goetheanisticos
Rua Amaro Alves do Rosario 102
04884 São Paulo

Finland
Art therapy:
Arte-Mhisia School
Puuskakuja 14, 00850 Helsinki

Germany
Full-time seminar over two terms for doctors and medical students:
Anthroposophisches Ärzte Seminar
Haberschlaiheide 1, 70794 Filderstadt

Full nursing training:
Freie Krankenpflegeschule an der
Filderklinik
Haberschlaiheide 1, 70794 Filderstadt
Ausbildungsinstitut für Krankenpflege
Klinikum der Universität
Witten/Herdecke
Beckweg 4, 58313 Herdecke

Postgraduate anthroposophical nursing:
Fortbildungsinstitut für Kranken-
und Altenpflege
Johann Kepler Str. 19, 753783 Bad
Liebenzell

*Rhythmical massage and hydrotherapy
courses (in English and German):*
Margarethe Hauschke Schule
Grübinger Strasse 29, 73087 Bad Boll

Eurythmy therapy:
Berufsverband Heileurythmie
Roggenstrasse 82, 70794 Filderstadt

Artistic therapy:
Artaban Schule,
Westfälischestrasse 82. 10709 Berlin

Margarethe Hauschka Schule
Grübinger Strasse 29, 73087 Bad Boll

Seminar für Kunstlerische Therapie
Mühlweg 18-20, 89143 Blaubeuren

Music therapy:
Anny von Lange Schule
Alfredstrasse 37, 20535 Hamburg

Musiktherapeutische Arbeitstätte
Arno Holz Strasse 16, 12165 Berlin

Speech therapy:
Christa Slezak-Schindler
Johann Kepler Str. 10, 7263 Bad
Liebenzell

Netherlands

*Ten-day introductory course and one-year
postgraduate course for doctors and medical students:*
De Vrije Hogeschool
Hoofdstraat 20, 3972 LA Driebergen

Eurythmy therapy:
Heileurythmie-Ausbildung
Gentsestraat 68, 2587 HW The Hague

Artistic therapy:
Academie de Wervel
Kon. Wilhelminalaan 2a, 3972 EX
Driebergen

Switzerland

*One-to-three-month courses (in English
and German) for doctors and medical
students:*
Ärztliche Fortbildungsstätte, Dr Rosselke
Zech
Grellingerweg 4, 4144 Arlesheim

One-year postgraduate nursing course:
Ita Wegman Klinik
Pfeffinger Weg 1, 4144 Arlesheim

Eurythmy therapy:
Heileurythmie Ausbildung am
Goetheanum
4143 Dornach

Sculpture therapy:
Ausbildungs und Arbeitsstätte für plas-
tisch-künstlerische Therapie
Postfach 134, 4143 Dornach

Speech therapy:
Ursula Ostermai
Postfach 701, 4144 Arlesheim

Index